The Open
University

MU123
Discovering mathematics

BOOK C
Units 8–10

This publication forms part of an Open University module. Details of this and other Open University modules can be obtained from the Student Registration and Enquiry Service, The Open University, PO Box 197, Milton Keynes MK7 6BJ, United Kingdom (tel. +44 (0)845 300 60 90; email general-enquiries@open.ac.uk).

Alternatively, you may visit the Open University website at www.open.ac.uk where you can learn more about the wide range of modules and packs offered at all levels by The Open University.

To purchase a selection of Open University materials visit www.ouw.co.uk, or contact Open University Worldwide, Walton Hall, Milton Keynes MK7 6AA, United Kingdom for a brochure (tel. +44 (0)1908 858779; fax +44 (0)1908 858787; email ouw-customer-services@open.ac.uk).

The Open University, Walton Hall, Milton Keynes MK7 6AA.

First published 2010. Second edition 2014.

Edited, designed and typeset by The Open University, using the Open University TeX System.

Printed in the United Kingdom by Henry Ling Limited, at the Dorset Press, Dorchester DT1 1HD

ISBN 978 1 7800 7865 6

2.1

Contents

UNIT 8   Geometry   7

Introduction   8

1 Angles   9
   1.1 Angles and lines   9
   1.2 Pairs of equal angles   12

2 Shapes and symmetry   17
   2.1 Triangles   17
   2.2 Polygons   23
   2.3 Symmetry   27

3 Congruent and similar shapes   28
   3.1 Congruent triangles   30
   3.2 Similar triangles   38
   3.3 Pythagoras' Theorem   43

4 Perimeters and areas   48
   4.1 Finding perimeters and areas   48
   4.2 Using perimeters and areas   52
   4.3 Circles and π 54

5 Solids   58
   5.1 Some standard solids   58
   5.2 Volumes and surface areas of solids   60
   5.3 Using volumes and surface areas   62

Learning checklist   63

Solutions and comments on Activities   64

UNIT 9   Expanding algebra   71

Introduction   72

1 Number patterns and algebra   72
   1.1 Arithmetic sequences   72
   1.2 Another number pattern   79

2 Multiplying out pairs of brackets   81
   2.1 Pairs of brackets   81
   2.2 Squaring brackets   84
   2.3 Differences of two squares   86

Contents

3 Quadratic expressions and equations   **87**

3.1 Quadratic expressions   87

3.2 Quadratic equations   88

3.3 Solving simple quadratic equations   90

3.4 Factorising quadratics of the form $x^2 + bx + c$ 91

3.5 Solving quadratic equations by factorisation   95

3.6 Factorising quadratics of the form $ax^2 + bx + c$ 97

3.7 Problems leading to quadratic equations   100

4 Manipulating algebraic fractions   **103**

4.1 Equivalent algebraic fractions   103

4.2 Adding and subtracting algebraic fractions   105

4.3 Multiplying and dividing algebraic fractions   107

5 Rearranging formulas   **109**

5.1 Solving equations by clearing algebraic fractions   110

5.2 Rearranging formulas by clearing algebraic fractions   112

5.3 Formulas involving powers   115

Learning checklist   **117**

Solutions and comments on Activities   **118**

UNIT 10   Quadratics   **125**

Introduction   **126**

1 Introducing parabolas   **126**

1.1 Parabolas everywhere   127

1.2 Projectiles   132

1.3 Stopping distances   136

2 Graphs of quadratic functions   **138**

2.1 Graphs of equations of the form $y = ax^2$ 139

2.2 Graphs of equations of the form $y = ax^2 + bx + c$ 141

2.3 The intercepts of a parabola   143

2.4 Sketch graphs of quadratic functions   144

3 Solving quadratic equations   **148**

3.1 Solving quadratic equations graphically   148

3.2 The quadratic formula   152

3.3 The number of solutions of a quadratic equation   156

3.4 Vertically-launched projectiles   158

4 Completing the square — **160**

4.1 Shifting parabolas — 160

4.2 Completing the square in quadratics of the form
$x^2 + bx + c$ — 164

4.3 Solving quadratic equations by completing the square — 167

4.4 Completing the square in quadratics of the form
$ax^2 + bx + c$ — 169

5 Maximisation problems — **172**

5.1 The maximum height of a vertically-launched
projectile — 172

5.2 Maximising yields — 174

5.3 Maximising areas — 177

Learning checklist — **179**

Solutions and comments on Activities — **180**

ACKNOWLEDGEMENTS — **188**

INDEX — **189**

Geometry

Introduction

Geometry is the study of angles, lines, shapes and solids. The word is derived from the Greek words 'geo' (earth) and 'metria' (measurement), and geometry has been used for thousands of years for measuring land, navigating, and mapping the world and the stars. It is now used in many different applications, from global positioning satellites to computer graphics and cosmology (the study of the physical universe as a whole).

A number of ancient Greek mathematicians laid the foundations of geometry. You may have heard of one of the foremost of them.

Much of the content of Euclid's *Elements* was the core of school geometry in the UK until about 1970.

Euclid was a Greek mathematician who worked in the city of Alexandria in Egypt in the third century BC. Little is known about his life other than that he produced ten works, of which five have survived to the present day. His reputation as a mathematician is based on his main work, the *Elements*, which was the standard introduction to mathematics for over two thousand years. It is claimed to be the best-selling mathematics book of all time, and is one of the most frequently printed books ever.

The following activity looks at Euclid's *Elements*.

 Video

Activity I *Learning about Euclid's Elements*

Watch the video *Euclid's Elements*.

One reason why the *Elements* was so important was that it introduced generations of mathematicians to ideas of rigorous proof. It starts with a small number of **axioms** (truths that were taken as self-evident), such as the fact that a straight line can be drawn between any two points. It then proceeds to prove theorems, such as Pythagoras' Theorem (which you will meet in Section 3), using nothing more than the axioms and previously proven theorems. This approach was very influential in the development of mathematics.

Although it isn't possible to take such a formal approach here, you will see some examples of proving geometric theorems by using definitions and previously established results. This will give you a taste of the way that geometry was developed in Euclid's *Elements*.

Section 1 introduces you to some geometric terminology and some important properties of angles between straight lines that you will be using throughout the rest of the unit. Section 2 concentrates on the properties of polygons – shapes with straight sides – and symmetry. In both Sections 1 and 2, you will be referred to some dynamic geometry software that allows you to explore geometric diagrams interactively, before looking at more rigorous proofs.

Section 3 considers when two shapes are essentially the same and introduces the ideas of congruency and similarity. These are useful both in practical applications such as constructing buildings and bridges, and in proving general properties of shapes.

"I THINK YOU SHOULD BE MORE EXPLICIT HERE IN STEP TWO."

The perimeters and areas of shapes are considered in Section 4. A modern application discussed here is the detection of abnormal cells in tissue samples by computer-assisted classification. You will also see Archimedes' method for calculating approximations for the constant π, which occurs in the formulas for the perimeter and area of a circle.

Finally, Section 5 looks at how to calculate the volume and the surface area of a solid object.

If you would like some extra practice with some of the ideas in this unit, then have a look at Maths Help Module 7: Geometry.

In 1706 the English mathematician William Jones introduced the use of π to mean the ratio of the circumference of a circle to its diameter, but the symbol didn't come into general use until it was popularised by Leonhard Euler in his *Introductio in analysin infinitorum* in 1748.

1 Angles

1.1 Angles and lines

This subsection introduces some terminology and notation that are useful for explaining geometric ideas clearly and concisely. You may like to make a note of any terms that you have not met before, so that you can refer to them easily as you work through the unit.

Let's start with some definitions. In geometry, a **point** has a position but no size. For example, the place where two lines cross (or two line segments meet) is a point. In Figure 1, six points are labelled with the upper-case letters A, B, C, D, E and F.

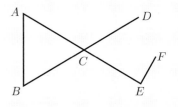

Figure 1 Points and line segments

A **line** is a straight line, as normally understood, but one that extends infinitely far in both directions. A finite portion of a line, which is all that you can draw in practice, is called a **line segment**. There are several line segments in Figure 1, such as the one between the points A and B, which is referred to as AB (or BA). Line segments are often just called lines, for brevity. A point where two line segments meet or cross is called a **vertex**. So in Figure 1 there are vertices at A, B, C and E.

In MU123 you may assume that any line segment drawn in a diagram is a straight line, even where a point along its length is identified. For example, in Figure 1, assume that ACE and BCD are both straight lines.

The plural of *vertex* is *vertices*.

Angles are a measure of rotation and can be measured in **degrees**. There are 360 degrees (written as 360°) in a full turn, and therefore there are 180° in a half-turn and 90° in a quarter-turn or **right angle**. In Figure 1, if the line segment EF is rotated through a quarter-turn anticlockwise, then it lies in the same direction as the line segment EC, so the angle between EF and EC is a right angle. This angle can be referred to as $\angle FEC$ or $F\hat{E}C$ (or $\angle CEF$ or $C\hat{E}F$).

In fact, there are *two* angles determined by the line segments FE and EC, one of 90° and one of 270°, as indicated by the small arcs in Figure 2. The notations $\angle FEC$ and $F\hat{E}C$ refer to the smaller angle.

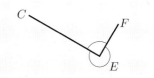

Figure 2 Two angles determined by the line segments FE and EC

$\angle FEC$ and $F\hat{E}C$ are both read as 'angle F E C'.

Finally, a **plane** is a flat surface that extends infinitely far in all directions. For example, a flat piece of paper is part of a plane.

Sometimes it is cumbersome to use several letters to refer to a line segment or angle, and in Figure 3 some line segments and angles have been labelled with single letters. The letters a and b have been used to label two line segments, and the Greek letters θ, ϕ and ψ have been used to label three angles, which are also marked with small arcs to help you to identify them. Also included in the diagram is the special square symbol that indicates a right angle. It has been used to mark $\angle CEF$ as a right angle.

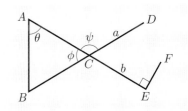

Figure 3 Line segments and angles labelled with single letters

Greek letters are often used to label angles. Some Greek letters that are used frequently are listed in Table 1, with their spellings and pronunciations. A full table of Greek letters is included in the Handbook.

Table 1 Some Greek letters

α	alpha	θ	theta (pronounced '*thee*-ta')
β	beta (pronounced '*bee*-ta')	ϕ	phi (pronounced '*fy*')
γ	gamma	ψ	psi (pronounced '*sigh*')
δ	delta	ω	omega (pronounced '*oh*-meh-ga')

The notation and symbols used for line segments and angles are also used to refer to the *lengths* of line segments and to the *sizes* of angles. So you can ask questions about Figure 3 such as: 'Is AB equal to BC?' or 'Is θ equal to $60°$?'

Angles can be classified into different types, as described in Table 2.

Table 2 Types of angle

Angle	Diagram	Description
Acute angle		Greater than $0°$ and less than $90°$
Right angle		Equal to $90°$
Obtuse angle		Greater than $90°$ and less than $180°$
Straight angle		Equal to $180°$
Reflex angle		Greater than $180°$ and less than $360°$

The mathematician and astronomer Hipparchus of Nicea (ca. 180–125 BC) is thought to have chosen 360 for the number of degrees in a full turn. Earlier, Babylonian astronomers had divided the day into 360 parts.

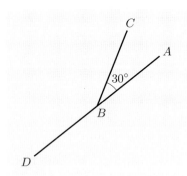

Figure 4 Two angles that add up to $180°$

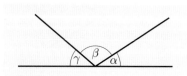

Figure 5 Three angles that add up to $180°$

Angles on a straight line

Since a straight angle is $180°$, any angles that together make up a straight angle add up to $180°$. For example, in Figure 4, $\angle ABC$ and $\angle CBD$ together add up to $180°$. So, since $\angle ABC = 30°$,

$$\angle CBD = 180° - 30° = 150°.$$

In Figure 5, the *three* angles α, β and γ add up to $180°$; that is, $\alpha + \beta + \gamma = 180°$.

The general result is summarised below.

Angles on a straight line add up to $180°$.

Many of the activities in this unit, and many of the applications of geometry, involve using a geometric diagram to deduce the sizes of angles or the lengths of line segments. When you do this, it is important to set out your solution clearly, justifying your results, as shown in the example below.

Example I   *Calculating angles*

(a) Calculate $\angle ABD$ in the diagram below.

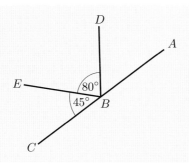

(b) Calculate the angle θ in the diagram below.

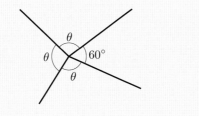

Solution

(a) ⚬ State the facts that you are going to use. ⚬

   ABC is a straight line, and angles on a straight line add up to $180°$.

   ⚬ Write down an equation involving the unknown angle, and solve it. ⚬

   So

   $$45° + 80° + \angle ABD = 180°$$
   $$\angle ABD = 180° - 80° - 45°$$
   $$\angle ABD = 55°.$$

(b) Angles in a full turn add up to $360°$. So

   $$\theta + \theta + \theta + 60° = 360°$$
   $$3\theta + 60° = 360°$$
   $$3\theta = 300°$$
   $$\theta = 100°.$$

You can write solutions to problems like those in Example 1 a little more concisely if you wish. For example, the solution to part (a) could be written with the justification in brackets like this:

   ABC is a straight line. So

   $$\angle ABD = 180° - 80° - 45° \quad \text{(angles on a straight line)}$$
   $$= 55°.$$

The following activities tie together some of the ideas that you've met in this subsection.

Activity 2   *Calculating angles*

This question is about the diagram below.

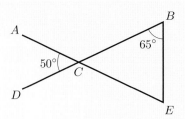

(a) Mark $\angle ACB$ as α and calculate its value.

(b) Which angles in the diagram are obtuse?

(c) Label the reflex angle at B as ω and calculate its value.

Activity 3   *Calculating angles of snooker balls*

When a snooker ball hits the cushion of a snooker table, the angle that its path makes with the cushion is the same after the impact as before. This angle is marked as θ in the diagram below. The diagram shows a path whose parts before and after impact make an angle of 110° with each other.

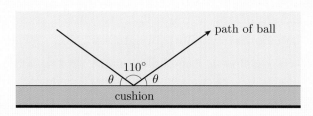

Calculate the angle θ in this case.

1.2   Pairs of equal angles

You have seen that you can sometimes deduce the sizes of angles from other angles that you already know. The next activity is about how you can do this in some particular situations. In the first part of the activity you will look at the angles formed when two lines cross each other, and in the second part you will consider the angles formed when a line crosses two parallel lines. As you saw in Unit 6, lines on a flat surface are *parallel* if they never cross even when extended infinitely far in each direction.

In a geometric diagram, parallel lines are indicated by putting matching arrowheads on the lines. When a diagram contains two pairs of parallel lines, one pair is marked with a single arrowhead on each line and the other pair is marked with a double arrowhead on each line. Figure 6 shows such a diagram.

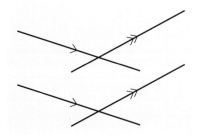

Figure 6   Two pairs of parallel lines

When you are looking at a geometric diagram, you should take care not to assume properties that are not marked. For example, you should not assume that two lines that *look* parallel really *are* parallel, unless they are marked with matching arrowheads.

Activity 4 *Exploring angles*

Dynamic geometry

Open the dynamic geometry resource for Unit 8.

(a) Click on the 'Opposite angles' tab and follow the instructions in the left-hand panel.

(b) Click on the 'Alternate angles' tab and follow the instructions.

The rest of this subsection explains the results in Activity 4 in more detail, and shows you how they can be useful.

Opposite angles

Figure 7 shows two lines, AC and DB, which cross. The angles θ and ϕ in this figure are called a pair of **opposite angles** or, more informally, **X angles**. The angles ψ and ω form a second pair of opposite angles.

In Activity 4(a) you saw that opposite angles seem to be equal. However, looking at some examples, as you did in this activity, isn't sufficient to show that this result is always true. What is needed is a more formal proof, using the same sort of rigorous argument that Euclid used.

Some resources use the phrase 'vertically opposite' to describe opposite angles, since they occur at a vertex.

Activity 5 *Proving Euclid's proposition about opposite angles*

This activity leads you through the steps in Euclid's proof that opposite angles are equal.

Consider the opposite angles θ and ϕ in Figure 7.

(a) The angles θ and ψ lie on the straight line BD. Use this fact to find an equation relating θ and ψ.

(b) The angles ϕ and ψ lie on the straight line AC. Use this fact to find an equation relating ϕ and ψ.

(c) Use algebra to show that $\theta = \phi$, by eliminating ψ from the equations found in parts (a) and (b).

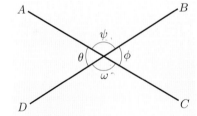

Figure 7 Two pairs of opposite angles

From Activity 5, we have the following result.

> Opposite angles are equal.

This is a useful result, as it means that as soon as you spot a pair of angles that are opposite to each other, you can deduce that they are equal. For example, in Figure 7, $\psi = \omega$.

Try using this result, and other facts that you have learned so far, in the next activity.

Activity 6   *Finding opposite angles*

Look at the diagram below, where the sizes of the angles inside triangle *ABC* are given.

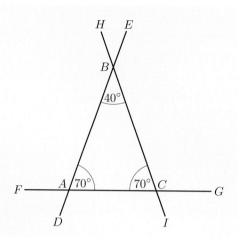

Find ∠*HBE*, ∠*FAD* and ∠*BAF*.

Corresponding and alternate angles

Now let's look at the angles formed when a line crosses a pair of parallel lines, as shown in Figure 8.

The angles α and β in Figure 8 are called **corresponding angles**, because they are in corresponding positions on the two parallel lines.

These angles are equal, because if you slide angle α up then it lies exactly on top of angle β, as you saw in Activity 4(b). Any corresponding angles can be seen to be equal in the same way, which gives the important result stated below.

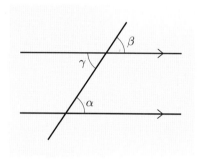

Figure 8   Corresponding and alternate angles

Corresponding angles are equal.

In Figure 9, two pairs of corresponding angles are marked on the same diagram (and there are two more pairs, which are not marked). One pair of corresponding angles is marked with single arcs, and a second pair is marked with double arcs. This is a convention used frequently in geometric diagrams when angles are not labelled with individual letters or with their sizes: equal angles are indicated by marking them with the same number of arcs.

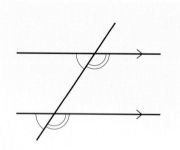

Figure 9   Two pairs of corresponding angles

The two angles marked with double arcs are part of a capital F, and so corresponding angles are also known informally as **F angles**.

Now look at Figure 8 again. The angles α and γ are known as **alternate angles**, because they are on alternate sides of the line that crosses the pair of parallel lines. They are also known informally as **Z angles**, because there is a pair of such angles in a capital Z.

You have seen that the angles α and β in Figure 8 are equal since they are corresponding angles. Also, the angles β and γ are equal since they are opposite angles, and hence the alternate angles α and γ are equal – you saw this argument in Activity 4. A similar argument applies to other pairs of alternate angles, so we have the following result.

Alternate angles are equal.

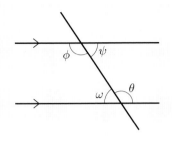

Figure 10   Two pairs of alternate angles

Not all pairs of alternate angles *look* like angles in a letter Z! For example, in Figure 10 the two angles marked θ and ϕ are obtuse angles, but they are alternate angles nevertheless. The angles marked ψ and ω are also alternate angles.

The next example illustrates how the results about angles that you have met in this subsection can be used to find unknown angles.

Example 2   *Finding corresponding and alternate angles*

Calculate the angles α and β in the diagram below.

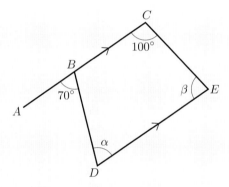

Solution

💬 Look for alternate, corresponding and opposite angles. 💬

The line segments AC and DE are parallel, so $\angle ABD$ and $\angle BDE$ are alternate angles.

So $\alpha = 70°$.

💬 Add a line segment to the diagram to help you spot equal angles. 💬

Extend CE to a point F, as shown in the margin. Then since AC and DE are parallel, $\angle DEF$ and $\angle BCE$ are corresponding angles. Since $\angle BCE = 100°$, it follows that $\angle DEF = 100°$.

Since β and $\angle DEF$ are angles on a straight line,

$$\beta = 180° - \angle DEF = 180° - 100° = 80°.$$

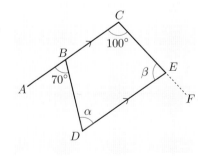

When you work on a problem like that in Example 2, you will probably find it helpful to mark the sizes of the angles on the diagram as you find them.

Here is an activity on equal angles.

Activity 7   *Finding angles equal to a given angle*

In the diagram below, $\angle DEG = 50°$ (this is marked on the diagram).

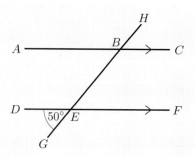

Which other angles in the diagram are equal to 50°, and why?

The result about alternate angles that you have met in this subsection can be stated as follows. Suppose that two lines are crossed by a third line, as shown in Figure 11. The result (in terms of the diagram in Figure 11) is:

If the first two lines are parallel, then the angles α and β are equal.

This result also works in reverse, in the sense that what is known as the *converse* result is true:

If the angles α and β are equal, then the first two lines are parallel.

In general, the **converse** of the result 'If A is true, then B is true' is the result 'If B is true, then A is true'.

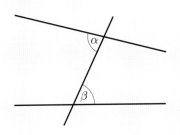

Figure 11   Two lines and a third line crossing them. Two angles are labelled α and β, respectively.

There is an important point here. A large proportion of mathematical results are of the form 'If A is true, then B is true' – and it is *not always the case* that the converse of a result is also a mathematical result. For example, if the last digit of a number is 2, then the number is even; this is a mathematical result. But the converse 'If a number is even, then its last digit is 2' is false, since (for instance) 14 is even.

Activity 8   *Finding an angle*

In the diagram below, the three angles marked θ are equal. Find the angle marked ϕ.

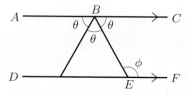

In this section you have seen how to use some results about angles to find the sizes of unknown angles. The same results can be used to prove general facts about shapes, as you will see in the next section.

2 Shapes and symmetry

2.1 Triangles

This subsection is all about triangles. You can refer to a triangle by using vertex labels. For example, the triangle in Figure 12 is referred to as triangle ABC. The notation $\triangle ABC$ is often used for brevity.

The **interior angles** of a triangle are the angles formed inside the triangle by its sides. For example, the interior angles of the triangle in Figure 12 are marked as α, β and γ. You may be familiar with the fact that the interior angles of every triangle add up to 180°. In the next activity you are asked to check this result for some triangles, and then prove it by using results that you found earlier.

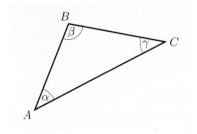

Figure 12   The interior angles of a triangle

Dynamic geometry

Activity 9   *Investigating the interior angles of a triangle*

Open the Unit 8 dynamic geometry resource, click on the 'Triangle' tab, and follow the instructions in the left-hand panel.

The result found in Activity 9 is as follows.

> The angles in a triangle add up to 180°.

The proof in Activity 9 is one of the most famous proofs in mathematics! It's worth thinking about the process of finding a proof like this in a bit more detail.

First, a key step was experimenting with the triangle, spotting a pattern and deciding what result seems to be true in general. Then, using results that were already proven, and working step by step with a clear diagram, it was possible to prove the result.

The idea of adding a line to the triangle is one that may not have occurred to you, although you have had a small taste of this in Example 2. An addition to a geometric diagram, in order to help prove a fact about the original shape, is known as a **construction**. A construction that is a line is known as a **construction line**. The extra line added to the diagram in Activity 9 is an example of a construction line. Adding construction lines to a geometric diagram can be a very powerful technique.

Once you have come up with the main ideas of a proof, the next stage is to write the proof out clearly, using words and mathematical notation, so that a reader can understand it. You must give an argument that refers to results known to be true, and work logically step by step from what you know to what you want to prove. The process of setting out a geometric argument is summarised overleaf, and then Example 3 shows how it is applied to prove that the angles in a triangle add up to 180°.

Setting out a geometric argument

1. State the general fact that is to be proved, including any given information.

2. Draw a diagram that contains the information that is given, labelling the important features, such as points and angles.

3. Add any useful constructions.

4. Proceed step by step from what is given to what is to be proved, explaining your reasoning clearly.

Example 3 *Proving the result about the angles in a triangle*

Prove that the angles of any triangle add up to $180°$.

Solution

💭 State the general fact to be proved. 💭

Here we prove that the angles in a triangle add up to $180°$.

💭 Draw a suitably-labelled diagram containing the information that you know. 💭

Consider $\triangle ABC$.

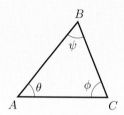

💭 Add any necessary constructions. 💭

Draw a line through B, parallel to the side AC.

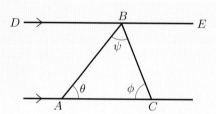

💭 Proceed step by step from what you know to the fact that is to be proved. Explain each step clearly. 💭

$\angle DBA$ and $\angle BAC$ are alternate angles. Therefore $\angle DBA = \theta$.

$\angle EBC$ and $\angle BCA$ are alternate angles. Therefore $\angle EBC = \phi$.

$\angle DBA$, $\angle ABC$ and $\angle EBC$ are on the straight line passing through B and so add up to $180°$.

So $\theta + \psi + \phi = 180°$.

But this is the sum of the angles in $\triangle ABC$.

Thus the angles in a triangle add up to $180°$.

You will be looking at some more proofs later in the unit, but in the rest of this subsection you will see how the result about the sum of the angles in a triangle can be used in different situations. First we look at two special types of triangle: *equilateral* and *isosceles* triangles.

'Isosceles' is pronounced 'eye-*sos*-eh-lees'.

If a triangle has all its sides the same length, then all its angles are equal and the triangle is known as an **equilateral triangle**. On a geometric diagram, you can show that two or more line segments have the same length by putting a stroke, or the same number of strokes, on each of the line segments, as shown in Figure 13.

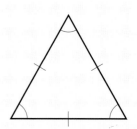

Activity 10   *The angles of an equilateral triangle*

Show that each angle in an equilateral triangle is 60°.

Figure 13   An equilateral triangle

The result that you were asked to show in Activity 10 is worth remembering, so it is stated formally below.

Each angle of an equilateral triangle is 60°.

If a triangle has just *two* sides that are the same length, then it also has two equal angles, known as the **base angles**, and the triangle is called an **isosceles triangle**. As shown in Figure 14, the third angle is known as the **apex angle**.

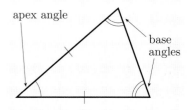

A triangle in which one angle is equal to 90° is called a **right-angled triangle**. Example 4 considers the angles in a right-angled triangle that is also isosceles.

Figure 14   An isosceles triangle

Example 4   *Finding angles in an isosceles triangle*

Calculate the base angles in an isosceles right-angled triangle, such as the one shown below.

The word 'isosceles' comes from the Greek *isos* (same) and *skelos* (leg).

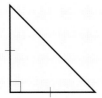

Solution

💭 Start from what you know. 💭

Let each base angle of the triangle be θ (the same letter can be used for each angle since the angles are equal). Then the angles of the triangle are 90°, θ and θ.

Using the fact that the angle sum of a triangle is 180° gives the equation

$$90° + 2\theta = 180°.$$

💭 Solve the equation. 💭

Rearranging the equation gives

$$2\theta = 180° - 90°$$
$$2\theta = 90°$$
$$\theta = 45°.$$

So each base angle of the triangle is 45°.

Now try the following activity.

Activity 11   Finding angles in isosceles triangles

(a) Each base angle of an isosceles triangle is 62°. What is the apex angle?

(b) The apex angle of an isosceles triangle is 30°. What are the base angles?

If you can show that two angles in a triangle are equal to each other, then you can deduce that the triangle is isosceles (or possibly equilateral) and that the sides opposite these two angles have the same length.

A triangle that is neither equilateral nor isosceles is known as a **scalene triangle**. All its sides are of different lengths.

The next example involves putting together several results that you have met so far. You will see that the steps of drawing a diagram, adding construction lines and working logically apply here too. The example involves finding some unknown angles: each new angle is found using information that was either known at the start or worked out earlier in the solution.

Tutorial clip

Example 5   Finding angles related to a garden shed

The diagram below shows the front of a garden shed, including a wooden strip that needs to be replaced. A close-up of the replacement strip is shown in the inset. The strip makes an angle of 65° with the vertical. The lines AB and DC are parallel, and the lines AE and BC (being vertical) are also parallel. Calculate the angles α, β, γ and δ.

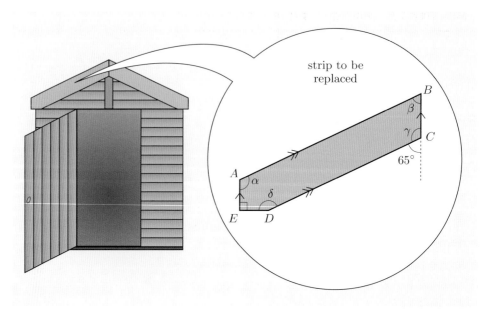

Solution

💭 Use the angle properties of straight lines, parallel lines and angles. 💭

Since the angles on a straight line add up to 180°,

$$\gamma = 180° - 65° = 115°.$$

Since the lines DC and AB are parallel, the angles marked β and 65° are corresponding angles. So

$$\beta = 65°.$$

💭 Draw construction lines to help you to find the unknown angles. 💭

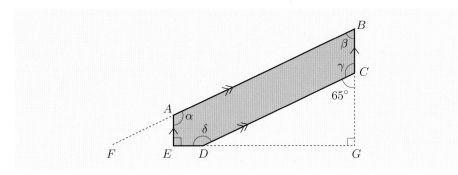

Since the lines AE and BC are parallel, $\angle FAE$ and $\angle ABC$ are corresponding angles. So $\angle FAE = \beta = 65°$.

Since the angles on a straight line add up to 180°,

$$\alpha = 180° - 65° = 115°.$$

Since the angles in $\triangle CGD$ add up to 180°,

$$\angle CDG = 180° - 90° - 65° = 25°.$$

Hence, since the angles on a straight line add up to 180°,

$$\delta = 180° - 25° = 155°.$$

The following activity asks you to go through a similar process to find some unknown angles in another diagram. There are often many different ways of finding unknown angles, and you may find a different way from that in the given solution.

Activity 12 *More angles related to the shed*

The wooden strip on the shed in Example 5 is one of a pair, as shown in the diagram below. Each of the two strips is at an angle of 65° to the vertical, and where they join there is a vertical strip, labelled as $KCJIH$ in the diagram below. This diagram extends the labelling notation that was used in Example 5. Find $\angle HKC$, $\angle KCJ$ and $\angle CJI$.

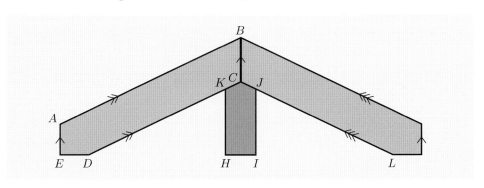

In Example 5 and Activity 12, the unknown angles were found by using known angles and working systematically around the diagrams. If no angles, or not enough angles, in a diagram are known, then it is sometimes useful to use letters to label one or more of the angles, and then find *expressions* for the other angles in terms of those letters.

Example 6   *Finding an expression for an angle*

Find an expression for $\angle ABC$ in the triangle below in terms of α.

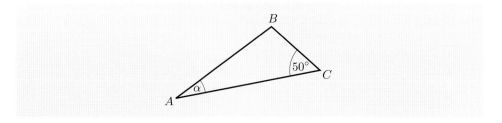

Solution

Since the sum of the angles in a triangle is 180°,

$$\angle ABC + 50° + \alpha = 180°.$$

Hence

$$\angle ABC = 180° - 50° - \alpha$$

so

$$\angle ABC = 130° - \alpha.$$

$\angle ABC$ can now be labelled as $130° - \alpha$ on the diagram.

Here is a similar activity for you to try.

Activity 13   *Finding angles in terms of a variable angle*

For each of the following diagrams, find $\angle ABC$ in terms of θ.

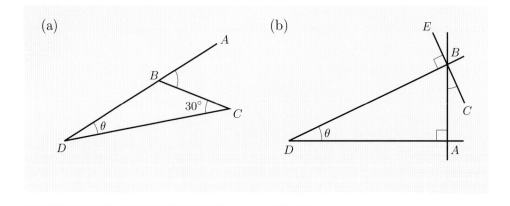

Next, you are asked to use the dynamic geometry resource to discover something about the sum of the *exterior angles* of a triangle. An **exterior angle** of a triangle is the angle formed outside the triangle by one side and an extension of the **adjacent** side, as illustrated in Figure 15.

Activity 14   *Investigating the exterior angles of a triangle*

Open the Unit 8 dynamic geometry resource and click on the 'Exterior angles' tab. Follow the instructions in the left-hand panel, and make a conjecture about the sum of the exterior angles in any triangle.

Prove your conjecture.

Dynamic geometry

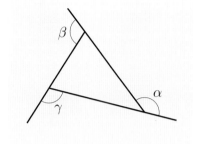

Figure 15   Exterior angles of a triangle

2.2 Polygons

A triangle has just three sides, but there are plenty of geometric shapes with more than three. A **polygon** is a plane shape with straight sides – so triangles and squares are examples of polygons. In particular:

- A **quadrilateral** is a polygon with four sides.
- A **pentagon** is a polygon with five sides.
- A **hexagon** is a polygon with six sides.

Similarly, **heptagons**, **octagons**, **nonagons** and **decagons** are polygons with, respectively, 7, 8, 9 and 10 sides. Figure 16 shows a few polygons.

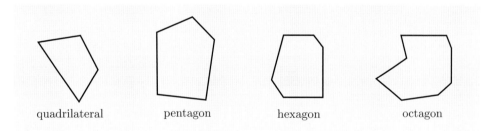

quadrilateral   pentagon   hexagon   octagon

Figure 16   Some polygons

You have already seen some names that are used to describe different types of triangles: *equilateral triangle*, *isosceles triangle* and *scalene triangle*. Table 3 (overleaf) shows examples of some types of quadrilaterals and their associated properties.

In this table, and in places in the rest of the unit, **opposite angles** means the *internally opposite* angles of a quadrilateral. These are the angles not at the ends of the same side: in the quadrilateral $ABCD$ in Figure 17, the angles at A and C are internally opposite, as are those at B and D. (Note that this is a different concept of 'opposite' from the opposite angles in Section 1, which share a vertex. It is usually clear from the context which type of opposite angles is meant.)

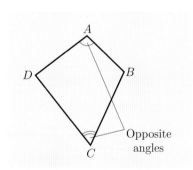

Figure 17   A pair of opposite angles in a quadrilateral

Table 3   Some special types of quadrilaterals

Shape	Diagram	Description
Square		Four equal sides and four right angles; opposite sides are parallel
Rectangle		Four right angles; opposite sides are equal and parallel
Parallelogram		Opposite sides are equal and parallel; opposite angles are equal
Rhombus		Four equal sides; opposite sides are parallel; opposite angles are equal
Kite		Two pairs of adjacent equal sides; one pair of opposite equal angles
Trapezium		One pair of parallel opposite sides

From Table 3 you can see that squares, rectangles and rhombuses are all special types of parallelogram.

Not all the properties in Table 3 are necessary to *define* the different types of quadrilateral. For example, a parallelogram can be defined to be a quadrilateral whose opposite sides are parallel, and the additional properties that opposite sides are equal and opposite angles are equal can be proved using this definition. In the next activity, you are asked to use the dynamic geometry resource to see how the property that opposite angles are equal can be proved. Later in the unit you will see how, if a kite is defined as a quadrilateral with two pairs of adjacent equal sides, then it can be proved that a kite also has one pair of opposite equal angles.

The properties of types of triangles, such as the property that an isosceles triangle has two equal angles, can be deduced from their definitions, in a similar way.

Activity 15   *Investigating the angles of a parallelogram*

Dynamic geometry

Open the Unit 8 dynamic geometry resource and follow the instructions in the 'Parallelogram' tab to see how to prove that opposite angles in a parallelogram are equal.

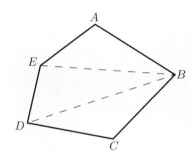

You saw earlier that the interior angles of any triangle add up to 180°. The sum of the interior angles of a polygon with more than three sides can be found by dividing the interior of the polygon into triangles.

For example, Figure 18 shows a pentagon divided into three triangles. The angle sum of each of the three triangles ($\triangle BCD$, $\triangle BDE$ and $\triangle ABE$) is 180°. But each angle in each triangle is an angle in the pentagon or a part of one of these angles. For example, $\angle ABC$ is divided into $\angle ABE$, $\angle EBD$ and $\angle DBC$. Moreover, each angle or part-angle in the pentagon belongs to one of the three triangles. So the angle sum of the pentagon is equal to the total angle sum of the three triangles, which is $3 \times 180° = 540°$.

Figure 18   A pentagon divided into three triangles

Activity 16   *Calculating the angle sum of a hexagon*

Calculate the angle sum of a hexagon by dividing its interior into triangles.

A polygon is said to be **regular** if its sides are of equal length and its interior angles are equal. Some regular polygons are shown in Figure 19. (The polygons in Figure 16 on page 23 are not regular.)

Regular quadrilaterals are called squares, and regular triangles are called equilateral triangles.

Figure 19   Some regular polygons

You can calculate the size of each angle of a regular polygon by dividing the total angle sum by the number of angles. For example, each angle in a regular pentagon is

$$\frac{540°}{5} = 108°.$$

Activity 17   *Finding the interior angles of a regular hexagon*

Calculate the interior angles of a regular hexagon.

Many geometric properties of shapes have practical applications. For example, in Mozambique farmers use geometric properties of rectangles to mark out the bases of their houses.

They use two equal lengths of rope tied together at their midpoints, and a piece of bamboo that is the width of the house that they plan to build. Two of the rope ends are attached to the ends of the bamboo, and the ropes are then pulled taut, as shown in Figure 20, making sure that each rope stays in a straight line. The endpoints of the ropes indicate the four corners of the house.

Source: Gerdes, P. (1988) 'On culture, geometrical thinking and mathematics education', *Educational Studies in Mathematics*, vol. 19, no. 2, pp. 137–62.

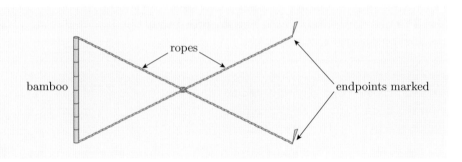

Figure 20   A device used in Mozambique for marking out a rectangle

The next activity asks you to explain why this method always gives a rectangle.

Activity 18   *Marking a rectangle for the base of a house*

In the diagram below, AB represents the piece of bamboo and BD and AC represent the ropes.

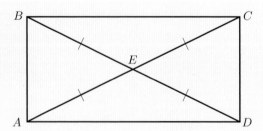

Remember that the only properties that you can assume are the four equal line segments marked, and the facts that AEC and BED are straight lines. For example, you can't assume that $\angle ABC$ is a right angle just because it looks like one. The fact that $\angle ABC$ is a right angle is the property that you're trying to *prove*! Similarly, you cannot assume that BC is parallel to AD.

(a) Explain why $\angle ABE = \angle BAE$ and $\angle EBC = \angle ECB$.

(b) Label $\angle ABE$ as α. Find expressions, in terms of α, for the following angles.

   (i) $\angle BAE$ (ii) $\angle AEB$ (iii) $\angle BEC$ (iv) $\angle EBC$

(c) By adding together the expressions for $\angle ABE$ and $\angle EBC$, show that $\angle ABC$ is a right angle.

(d) By a similar argument, the other interior angles of $ABCD$ can also be shown to be right angles. What can you deduce about the shape $ABCD$?

The dynamic geometry resource includes an optional activity, 'Semicircle', which you may like to look at if you would like further practice in proving geometric results. This activity explores the size of the angle $\angle BAC$ in Figure 21, where A is any point on the curved part of the semicircle.

2.3 Symmetry

Rotational symmetry

Some shapes have the property that if you rotate them through a fixed angle (less than a full turn) about a fixed point, then the rotated shape looks the same as the original shape. Such a shape is said to have **rotational symmetry**, and the fixed point is called the **centre of rotation**.

For example, if an equilateral triangle is rotated through one third of a full turn (120°) about its centre, then the rotated triangle looks the same as the original triangle, as shown in Figure 22. Since there are three positions in which the rotated triangle looks the same, it is said to have rotational symmetry of **order** 3, or three-fold **rotational symmetry**. Another way to think about the three-fold rotational symmetry of the triangle is that three rotations are needed to return it to its starting position.

All regular polygons have rotational symmetry. The order of the rotational symmetry is the same as the number of sides.

You can see many examples of rotational symmetry in nature. For example, a hibiscus flower (Figure 23) illustrates five-fold rotational symmetry, as you saw in the video for Unit 1.

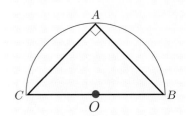

Figure 21 The angle in a semicircle

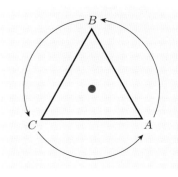

Figure 22 Rotating this equilateral triangle by 120° anticlockwise about its centre moves vertex A to vertex B, vertex B to vertex C, and vertex C to vertex A

Activity 19 *Spotting rotational symmetries*

For each of the following pictures, state the order of rotational symmetry.

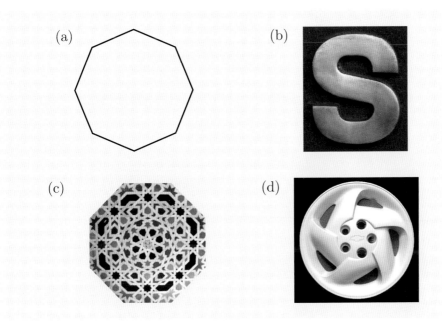

(a)

(b)

(c)

(d)

Figure 23 A hibiscus flower

Figure 24   Symmetry in the wings of butterflies

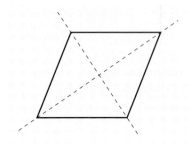

Figure 25   The two lines of symmetry of a rhombus

Line symmetry

Some shapes exhibit a different kind of symmetry, known as **line symmetry**, *mirror symmetry* or *reflectional symmetry*. For example, look at the first butterfly in Figure 24. If you were to fold the paper along an imaginary line down the centre of the stalk that the butterfly is resting on, then the pattern on one half of the butterfly would lie exactly on top of the pattern on the other half. Alternatively, if you place a mirror along this line, then the reflection gives the other half of the butterfly. This imaginary line is known as a **line of symmetry** (or a **reflection line** or *mirror line*). The second butterfly in Figure 24 also has a line of symmetry.

Shapes can have more than one line of symmetry. For example, a rhombus has two lines of symmetry, as shown in Figure 25.

Activity 20   *Symmetries of quadrilaterals*

Draw an example of each of the following quadrilaterals and mark in any lines of symmetry. (You may find it useful to refer back to Table 3 on page 24 for the main properties of these shapes.)

(a) A square

(b) A rectangle (that is not a square)

(c) A parallelogram (that is neither a rectangle nor a rhombus)

(d) A kite (that is not a rhombus)

In Units 10 and 12 you will see how line symmetry can be a useful way of describing some graphs.

In this section you have seen how to set out a geometric argument formally and explored some properties of polygons, as well as looking at some practical applications. The next section extends these ideas by looking at some more properties of triangles and how they can be used, both practically and theoretically.

3   Congruent and similar shapes

Geometric figures with the same size and shape are said to be **congruent**. So two shapes are congruent if you can pick one of the shapes up and place it exactly on top of the other shape, rotating or flipping over the first shape if necessary.

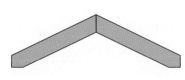

Figure 26   The wooden strips on the shed

You saw a pair of congruent shapes in Activity 12, which was about wooden strips on a garden shed. The shed is symmetrical, so the strip on the left-hand side is congruent to the strip on the right-hand side, as shown in Figure 26. Figure 27 shows some other pairs of congruent shapes.

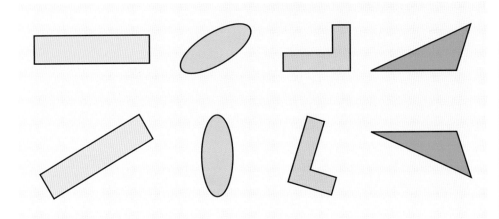

Figure 27   Four pairs of congruent shapes

Making congruent shapes, and checking that two shapes are congruent, occurs frequently in building and manufacturing. Since measuring sides and angles takes time, an important question to ask is: 'How many measurements are needed to make sure that two shapes are congruent?' Subsection 3.1 explores this question for *triangles*, and it uses some conditions for congruency of triangles to prove some geometric results. Triangles, and shapes made from triangles, are often used in constructions such as buildings and bridges, both to make the structures rigid and for an attractive design – examples are shown in Figures 28 and 29.

Figure 28   The Bank of China in Hong Kong

Geometric figures that have the same shape, but not necessarily the same size, are said to be **similar**. For example, if one shape is an enlargement of another (again, flipping is allowed), then the two shapes are similar, as illustrated in Figure 30.

Figure 30   Three similar shapes

As you saw in Unit 3, the factor by which the lengths in one shape are enlarged with respect to the lengths in a similar shape is called a **scale factor**. For example, each length in the second (flipped) 'F' shape in Figure 30 is about 1.5 times the corresponding length in the first 'F' shape, so the scale factor from the first shape to the second is about 1.5.

Figure 29   The Hearst Tower in New York

Subsection 3.2 investigates when two triangles are similar, and illustrates how similar triangles are used in practice. Then in Subsection 3.3 you will see how similar triangles can be used to prove one of the most well-known theorems in geometry – *Pythagoras' Theorem*.

3.1 Congruent triangles

Figure 31 shows three congruent triangles. Each of the first two triangles has its sides marked with one stroke, two strokes and three strokes in clockwise order, so either one of these triangles can be placed on top of the other without flipping. The sides of the third triangle have the same marks, but in anticlockwise order, so this triangle has to be flipped over before it can be placed on top of either of the other two.

Recall that strokes are used to indicate which side lengths are equal, and small arcs are used to indicate which angles are equal.

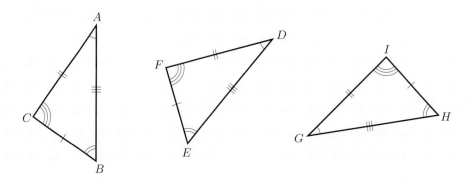

Figure 31   Three congruent triangles

When all the triangles are placed exactly on top of each other, the vertices A, D and G coincide, as do B, E and H, and also C, F and I. Vertices that can be made to coincide like this are said to be **corresponding vertices**. Since the angles marked with a single arc (at A, D and G) lie on top of each other, they are said to be **corresponding angles**. The angles marked with a double arc (at B, E and H) also form a set of corresponding angles, as do those marked with a triple arc (at C, F and I). (Note that this is a different use of the phrase 'corresponding angles' to earlier in the unit, where the same phrase referred to the F angles formed when a line crossed two parallel lines.)

The symbol $\cong$ is read as 'is congruent to'.

The symbol $\cong$ is used to indicate that two shapes are congruent. So you can write

$$\triangle ABC \cong \triangle DEF \cong \triangle GHI \tag{1}$$

to indicate that the three triangles in Figure 31 are congruent. In a statement like this, the order of the vertices indicates which vertices correspond. So statement (1) tells you that A, D and G correspond, as do B, E and H, and finally C, F and I.

Conditions for congruency

It might seem that to show that two triangles are congruent, you would need to gather six pieces of information for each triangle: three lengths and three angles. But how much of this information is actually needed to determine whether two triangles are congruent?

To work this out, let's consider how much information about a triangle you need to have in order for the triangle to be completely determined. In other words, let's look at how much information is needed to ensure that there is only one possible shape and size for the triangle.

The six possible pieces of information are the lengths of the three sides and the sizes of the three angles. Certainly it is not enough to know only one or two of these pieces of information. If you know the lengths of two sides of a triangle, or the sizes of two angles, or the length of one side and the size of one angle, then there is more than one possibility for the triangle.

For example, Figure 32 shows two different triangles, each of which has sides of lengths 2 cm and 3 cm.

So you certainly need at least three of the six possible pieces of information for the triangle to be determined. Let's consider the possible cases where you know three pieces of information.

You could know all three sides, all three angles, two sides and an angle or two angles and a side. The first of these cases is known as the *side-side-side* case (**SSS**), and the second is known as the *angle-angle-angle* case (**AAA**). Each of the third and fourth cases splits into two subcases, as follows.

If you know two sides and an angle, then the angle could be between the two sides – this is the *side-angle-side* case (**SAS**) – or it could be one of the other two angles – this is the *angle-side-side* case (**ASS**). Similarly, if you know two angles and a side, then the side could be between the two angles – this is the *angle-side-angle* case (**ASA**) – or it could be one of the other two sides – this is the *angle-angle-side* case (**AAS**).

Let's consider these six cases in turn.

The side-side-side case (SSS)

First, let's consider the case where the lengths of the sides of a triangle are known. Does this completely determine the triangle?

You might like to experiment with three lengths of paper. Try to arrange them into a triangle in any way possible, as shown in Figure 33. You will find that however much you try, there is essentially only one way to make a triangle. So if the side lengths of a triangle are known, then there is only one possibility for the shape and size of the triangle. (You will see how to calculate the angles from the lengths of the sides in Unit 12.)

This means that if you know that the lengths of the sides in one triangle are the same as the lengths of the sides in another triangle, then the two triangles are congruent, as shown in Figure 34: $\triangle ABC \cong \triangle DFE$.

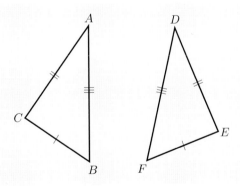

Figure 34 Two triangles that are congruent by SSS

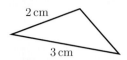

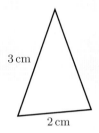

Figure 32 The lengths of two sides of a triangle do not constitute enough information to determine the triangle

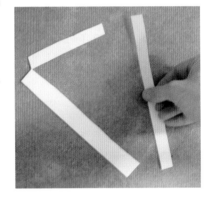

Figure 33 Trying to form a triangle

Side-side-side congruency of triangles is important in structural engineering. If you join together three rods to form a triangle, then the structure is rigid, even if the joints are hinges. Compare this with four rods joined to make a square – this structure changes shape easily. Many engineering lattice structures are made up of triangles.

Geometry started by appealing to physical intuition in situations such as this, but Euclid's approach in the *Elements* gave a method in which 'intuitively obvious' facts could be shown to be a logical consequence of more basic facts. This was a great step forward in mathematics.

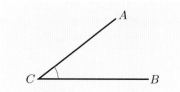

Figure 35   Two sides and an included angle

The side-angle-side case (SAS)

Consider the situation where you know the lengths of two sides of a triangle, together with the angle between them, which is called the **included angle**. This is illustrated in Figure 35. There is only one way to complete the triangle here, which is to draw the line from A to B. So the triangle is determined from this information.

So if two sides and the included angle of one triangle are equal to two sides and the included angle of another triangle, then the two triangles are congruent, as illustrated in Figure 36.

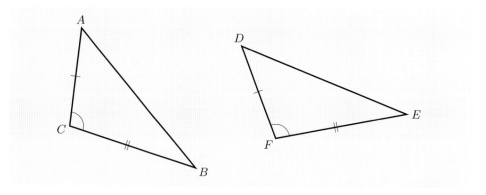

Figure 36   Two triangles that are congruent by SAS

The angle-side-angle case (ASA)

Suppose that you know two angles of a triangle and the side between them – the **included side** – as illustrated in Figure 37.

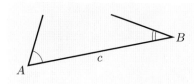

Figure 37   Two angles and the side between them

The point where the line segments from vertices A and B meet must be the third vertex of the triangle. So the triangle is determined by this information.

So if two angles and the side between them in one triangle are equal to two angles and the side between them in another triangle, then the triangles are congruent, as illustrated in Figure 38.

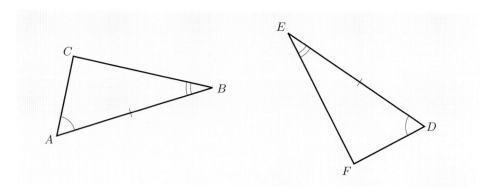

Figure 38   Two triangles that are congruent by ASA

The angle-angle-side case (AAS)

Consider the situation in which you know two angles of a triangle, as in the previous case, but instead of knowing the side *between* the angles, you know one of the other two sides. Since the third angle of the triangle can be calculated by using the fact that the sum of the angles is 180°, you still know two angles and the side between them, which is the previous case, and hence the triangle is determined.

So if you know that two angles and a side of a triangle in the order angle-angle-side are equal to two angles and a side of another triangle *in the same order*, then the triangles are congruent, as shown in Figure 39.

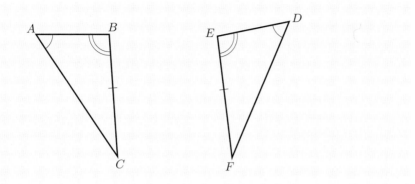

Figure 39   Two triangles that are congruent by AAS

You can check that the two triangles in Figure 39 have their equal angle-angle-side configurations in the same order by noticing that if you trace your finger around $\triangle ABC$ from the angle with one arc to the angle with two arcs, then the side with the stroke is next, and similarly if you trace your finger around $\triangle DEF$ from the angle with one arc to the angle with two arcs, then again the side with the stroke is next.

The angle-angle-angle case (AAA)

This is the situation where you know all three angles in a triangle. This is not enough to determine the triangle, because one triangle could be a scaled-up or scaled-down version of the other.

So if you know that the three angles in one triangle are the same as the three angles in another triangle, then you *cannot* conclude that the triangles are congruent.

The angle-side-side case (ASS)

If you know two sides and a non-included angle of a triangle, then there can be two possibilities for the triangle. This is illustrated in Figure 40, which shows that if you know the angle θ and the lengths of the sides a and b, then the third vertex F could be in either of the two positions shown.

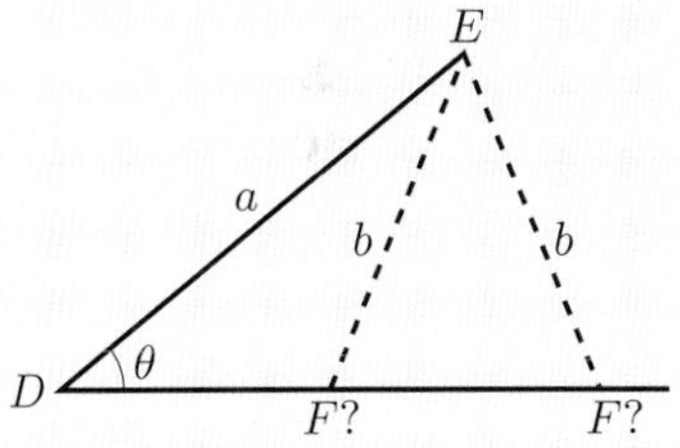

So if you know that two sides and a non-included angle of one triangle are equal to two sides and a non-included angle of another triangle, then you *cannot* conclude that the triangles are congruent.

Figure 40   Two possible triangles if angle θ and lengths a and b are known

Conclusion

All six possible cases of three pieces of information have now been covered. Four of them (SSS, SAS, ASA and AAS) show that two triangles are congruent, while the other two (AAA and ASS) do not guarantee congruency. These findings are summarised overleaf.

Strategy   *To check whether two triangles are congruent*

Two triangles are congruent if one of the following situations occurs.

- The three sides of one triangle are equal to the three sides of the other triangle (SSS).

- Two sides and the included angle of one triangle are equal to two sides and the included angle of another triangle (SAS).

- Two angles and the included side of one triangle are equal to two angles and the included side of another triangle (ASA).

- Two angles and a side of one triangle in the order angle-angle-side are equal to two angles and a side of the other triangle *in the same order* (AAS).

In fact, the ASA and AAS cases can be summarised as one criterion by using the idea of *corresponding sides*. If two triangles have the same three angles (as they do in the ASA and AAS cases), then a side in one triangle is said to **correspond** to a side in the other triangle if they are opposite equal angles. For example, in Figure 39 on page 33 the sides BC and EF are corresponding sides since they are opposite angles with one arc. Similarly, the sides AC and DF are corresponding sides, and the sides AB and DE are corresponding sides. The ASA and AAS cases can be summarised by saying that two triangles are congruent if two angles and a side of one triangle are equal to two angles and the *corresponding* side of the other triangle. You may prefer to use these conditions in this form.

Using the conditions for congruent triangles

You can practise using the strategy above in the next activity.

Activity 21   *Checking whether triangles are congruent*

For each of the following pairs of triangles, determine (if possible) whether the two triangles are congruent, explaining your answers.

In parts (a)–(c) of this activity no particular units are specified for the lengths of the sides of the triangles. This is often done in geometry, just as when we use coordinate axes we often don't specify particular units for the numbers on the axis scales.

Also, the diagrams are not drawn to scale, since this activity requires you to use the conditions for congruency rather than measurement.

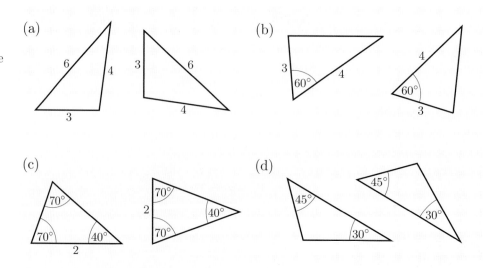

The next example illustrates that sometimes you need to find more angles before using one of the conditions to show that two triangles are congruent.

Example 7 *Showing that triangles are congruent*

 Tutorial clip

Show that the triangles below are congruent.

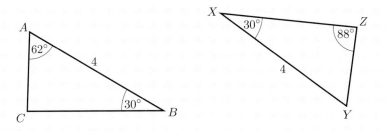

Solution

💭 Work out the unknown angle in $\triangle YXZ$, so that the angles of the two triangles can be compared. 💭

The interior angles of a triangle add up to 180°. So

$$\angle ZYX = 180° - 88° - 30° = 62°.$$

💭 Show that the triangles are congruent by using one of the conditions. 💭

In $\triangle ABC$ and $\triangle YXZ$:

- $\angle CAB = \angle ZYX$ (both angles are 62°)
- $AB = YX$ (both sides have length 4)
- $\angle ABC = \angle YXZ$ (both angles are 30°).

So $\triangle ABC \cong \triangle YXZ$ (by ASA).

💭 The condition AAS could have been used here as an alternative to ASA. 💭

Here is a similar activity for you to try.

Activity 22 *Showing that triangles are congruent*

Show that the two triangles in the diagram below are congruent.

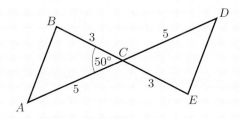

If you can prove that two triangles are congruent, then you can deduce that corresponding angles and sides are equal. This can be a powerful method for establishing properties of shapes. For example, a kite can be defined as a quadrilateral with two pairs of adjacent equal sides. In Table 3, it was stated that there is also a pair of opposite equal angles, but how does that follow from the definition?

In the next example you will see how this can be deduced using congruent triangles. The example involves two triangles that share a side. A side like this is called a **common side** of the triangles.

Example 8   *Proving that a kite has two opposite equal angles*

Use the fact that a kite is a quadrilateral with two pairs of adjacent equal sides to prove that it also has a pair of opposite equal angles.

Solution

💭 Draw a kite with vertices labelled A, B, C, D. Mark the equal sides: $AB = AD$, $BC = DC$. Then draw the diagonal AC as a helpful construction. Show that the two resulting triangles are congruent. 💬

The diagram below shows a kite with its two pairs of equal sides marked.

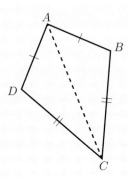

In $\triangle ABC$ and $\triangle ADC$:

- $AB = AD$ (given)
- $BC = DC$ (given)
- the side AC is common to both triangles.

So $\triangle ABC \cong \triangle ADC$ (by SSS).

💭 Now use facts about congruent triangles. 💬

Hence the corresponding angles of $\triangle ABC$ and $\triangle ADC$ are equal. The angles opposite AC are $\angle ABC$ in $\triangle ABC$ and $\angle ADC$ in $\triangle ADC$. So $\angle ABC = \angle ADC$.

That is, the kite has two opposite equal angles.

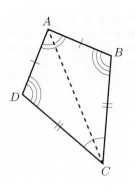

Figure 41   The kite in Example 7 with corresponding angles of congruent triangles marked

Congruent triangles can be used to prove even more properties of kites. For example, in Figure 41 the corresponding angles of the congruent triangles $\triangle ABC$ and $\triangle ADC$ are marked as equal. From this you can see another property: the diagonal AC **bisects** each of $\angle DAB$ and $\angle BCD$, that is, it cuts each of these angles into two equal parts. And this result leads on to further properties. If you draw the diagonal BD, congruent triangles can be used again to show that the diagonals cross each other at right angles. You might like to try this.

Congruent triangles can even help with a game of snooker! Figure 42 shows three balls on a snooker table. The player has to hit the white ball with the cue so that it strikes the red ball. The black ball is in the way, so this has to be achieved by bouncing the white ball off the cushion, as shown. The ball bounces off the cushion at the same angle as it strikes the cushion. These angles are both marked θ in Figure 42.

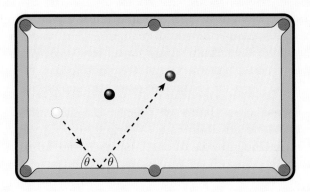

Figure 42   Balls on a snooker table

The player's problem is to decide the point where the white ball must strike the cushion if it is to hit the red ball. You are asked to look at the geometry of this problem in the next activity, and after the activity you will see that this gives the player a strategy for hitting the red ball.

Activity 23   *Investigating angles on a snooker table*

In the diagram below, the line indicating the initial path of the white ball has been extended, and a line has been drawn down from the position of the red ball, perpendicular to the cushion. The point D is the point where these two lines meet. As in Figure 42, the two equal angles between the cushion and the path of the white ball are both labelled as θ.

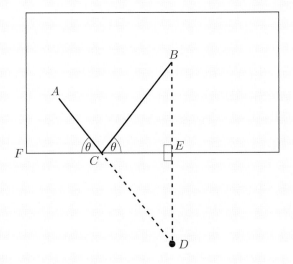

(a) Show that $\triangle BCE$ and $\triangle DCE$ are congruent.

(b) Deduce that the line segments BE and DE are equal.

So, from the solution to Activity 23, if the snooker player imagines the point that is the 'reflection' of the red ball in the cushion and hits the white ball in that direction, then it will bounce off the cushion and hit the red ball.

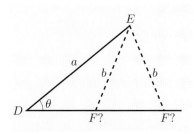

Figure 43   Two possible triangles if angle θ and lengths a and b are known

Finally in this subsection, let's briefly look at the ASS case again, which was one of the two cases that does not guarantee congruency. The diagram that illustrated this case is repeated in Figure 43. Remember that this diagram shows that if you know angle θ and the lengths of the sides a and b, then there could be two possibilities for the triangle, since the third vertex F could be in either of the two positions shown.

However if you also know that angle θ is a *right angle* or an *obtuse angle*, then there is only one possibility for the triangle. So if you know that two sides and a non-included angle of one triangle are equal to two sides and a non-included angle of another triangle, in the same order, and you also know that this angle is 90° or greater, then you *can* say that the triangles are congruent.

In this subsection you have used different conditions to show that two triangles are congruent, and you have used the congruence of triangles to deduce further results. In the next subsection, the same sort of approach is used to determine when two triangles are similar and how this property can be used in practice.

3.2   Similar triangles

Similar triangles are the same shape but not necessarily the same size. As with congruence, the triangles may be rotated or flipped over. For example, the two triangles in Figure 44 are similar to each other.

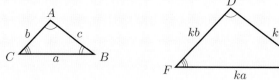

Figure 44   Two similar triangles

Any two similar triangles have the following properties:

- the three angles of one triangle are equal to the three angles of the other triangle;

- the three sides of one triangle are *in proportion* to the three sides of the other triangle.

The second property means that the three side lengths of one triangle are obtained from the three side lengths of the other triangle by multiplying by the same scale factor. In Figure 44 the scale factor from the first triangle to the second triangle is k.

Another way to think about the second property is that it means that the ratios of the sides of the two triangles are equal. For the triangles in Figure 44,

Alternatively, you can write
$$\frac{AB}{DE} = \frac{BC}{EF} = \frac{CA}{FD},$$
since all these ratios are equal to $1/k$.

$$\frac{DE}{AB} = \frac{EF}{BC} = \frac{FD}{CA}, \tag{2}$$

since all these ratios are equal to k.

To check whether two triangles are similar, you can check either of the two properties immediately below Figure 44 – the other property then holds automatically.

So if you know that two triangles have the same three angles, then they are similar and so they also have their sides in proportion. (This also holds if two angles in one triangle are equal to two angles in the other triangle, since then the third angles must also be equal.) This means that you can immediately write down equations like equations (2) for the triangles. The numerator and denominator of each equal ratio are sides that are opposite equal angles; that is, they are *corresponding sides*. Writing down these ratios is a useful way to find the lengths of unknown sides in similar triangles, as illustrated in the example below.

Similarly, if you know that two triangles have their sides in proportion, then they are similar and so they also have three equal angles. You can tell which angles are equal by using the fact that the sides on the numerator and denominator of each equal ratio are corresponding sides and therefore opposite equal angles.

Example 9 *Finding unknown side lengths in similar triangles*

Find the length of the side DE in the diagram below.

 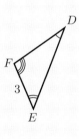

Solution

The diagram indicates that the two triangles have the same three angles, so they are similar.

Also, the sides BC and EF correspond, because they are opposite the angles marked with one arc, and similarly AC and DF correspond, and AB and DE correspond. Hence

$$\frac{EF}{BC} = \frac{DF}{AC} = \frac{DE}{AB}.$$

In particular,

$$\frac{EF}{BC} = \frac{DE}{AB}.$$

Substituting in the known lengths gives

$$\frac{3}{4} = \frac{DE}{7}.$$

Hence

$$DE = \frac{3 \times 7}{4} = \frac{21}{4} = 5\tfrac{1}{4}.$$

Here is a similar activity for you to try.

Activity 24   *Finding unknown side lengths in similar triangles*

The triangles below are similar. Calculate the lengths TS, RS, XZ and YX.

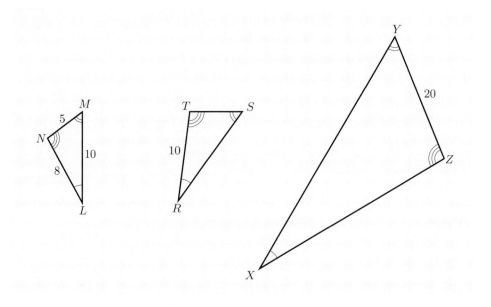

Angles or lengths in geometric diagrams can often be deduced by finding and using similar triangles. This is illustrated in the next example.

Example 10   *Finding an unknown side in similar triangles*

Find the length x in the diagram below.

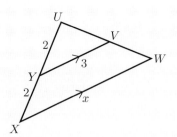

Solution

☁ Show that $\triangle UYV$ and $\triangle UXW$ are similar. ☁

The line segments YV and XW are parallel. So in $\triangle UYV$ and $\triangle UXW$:

Note that $\angle YUV$ is common to both triangles, and this fact could have been used instead of one of the facts here.

- $\angle UYV = \angle UXW$ (these are corresponding (F) angles)
- $\angle UVY = \angle UWX$ (these are corresponding (F) angles).

Since two angles in one triangle are equal to two angles in the other, $\triangle UYV$ is similar to $\triangle UXW$.

⚲ Write down the ratio of corresponding sides, preferably with the unknown side in the numerator. ⚲

The sides YV and XW are corresponding, since they are both opposite the common angle, $\angle YUV$. Similarly, UY and UX are corresponding, as are UV and UW. Hence

$$\frac{XW}{YV} = \frac{UX}{UY} = \frac{UW}{UV}.$$

Now, $UY = 2$ and $YX = 2$, so $UX = 2 + 2 = 4$. So

$$\frac{4}{2} = \frac{x}{3},$$

and hence

$$x = \frac{4 \times 3}{2} = 6.$$

Similar triangles can be used to determine lengths that cannot be easily measured, as the next activity illustrates. The activity shows you how to measure the height of a tree without having to climb a ladder with a tape measure. This method of measuring the heights of tall objects was used extensively in the sixteenth and seventeenth centuries!

Activity 25   *Finding the height of a tree*

Suppose that on a sunny day you place a stick in the ground near a tree, so that the length of the exposed part of the stick is 1 m. You then measure the lengths of the shadows cast by the stick and the tree, as shown below. The stick is placed at the same angle as the tree (in the diagram they are both vertical), and the ground is level.

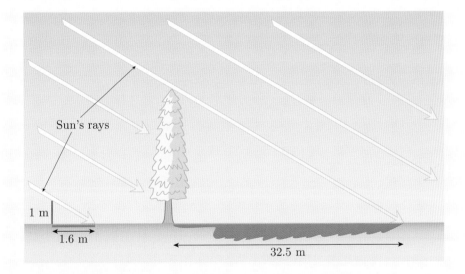

(a) Assuming that the rays of the Sun are parallel, show that the two triangles in the diagram are similar. (One triangle is formed by the stick, its shadow on the ground and a ray of the Sun; the other is formed by the tree, its shadow on the ground and a ray of the Sun.)

(b) Suppose that the length of the stick's shadow is 1.6 m and the length of the tree's shadow is 32.5 m. Calculate the height of the tree.

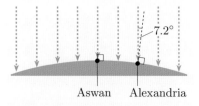

Figure 45 The Sun's rays at the same time at Aswan and Alexandria

The fact that the Sun's rays are parallel was used by Eratosthenes (who was mentioned in Unit 3) to estimate the size of the Earth. He knew (by observing shadows) that at noon at midsummer, the Sun's rays were vertical at Aswan in Egypt and at the same time were at an angle of 7.2° to the vertical at Alexandria, also in Egypt (Figure 45). The angle 7.2° is $\frac{1}{50}$ of a full turn, so he concluded that the distance from Alexandria to Aswan was $\frac{1}{50}$ of the circumference of the Earth. His estimate was remarkably accurate, but historians argue about how accurate, because no one is sure about the size of Eratosthenes' unit of length, the *stadion*.

Checking for similarity

There is a third useful way of showing that two triangles are similar. Suppose that two triangles have the property shown in Figure 46. They have one equal angle and the sides containing this angle are in proportion.

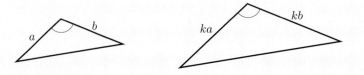

Figure 46 Two triangles with one equal angle and the sides containing this angle in proportion

This property guarantees that the triangles are similar. To see this, imagine scaling the first triangle in Figure 46 by the scale factor k. The scaled triangle will be similar to the first triangle, but it will also be congruent to the second triangle, by SAS. So the two triangles in Figure 46 are similar.

So you now have three ways to check whether two triangles are similar.

Strategy *To check whether two triangles are similar*

Two triangles are similar if any one of the following three conditions holds. Then the other two conditions also hold.

• The three angles of one triangle are equal to the three angles of the other triangle.

• The three sides of one triangle are in proportion to the three sides of the other triangle (their ratios are equal).

• An angle of one triangle is equal to an angle of the other triangle, and the sides containing these angles are in proportion (their ratios are equal).

Try using these conditions to see if you can spot which triangles are similar in the activity on the next page.

Activity 26   *Checking for similarity*

Which of the following pairs of triangles are pairs of similar triangles?
Assume only that they have the properties marked.

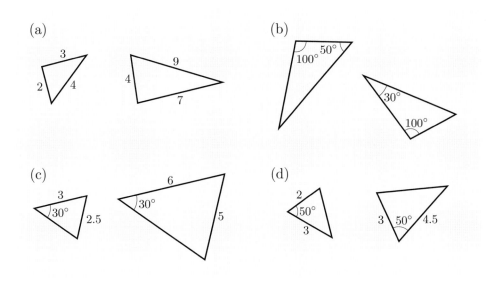

(a)

(b)

(c)

(d)

In the next subsection you will see how similar triangles can be used to
prove one of the most famous theorems in mathematics.

3.3 Pythagoras' Theorem

Pythagoras' Theorem is one of the oldest mathematical results known; it
involves the sides of a right-angled triangle. The longest side, which is
always the side opposite the right angle, is called the **hypotenuse**. This is
the side AB in Figure 47.

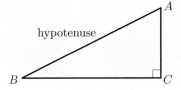

Figure 47   A right-angled
triangle

Pythagoras' Theorem

For a right-angled triangle, the square of the hypotenuse is equal to
the sum of the squares of the other two sides.

For example, for the right-angled triangle in Figure 47,

$$AB^2 = AC^2 + BC^2.$$

AB^2 is the notation used for the
square of the length AB.

Pythagoras' Theorem has long been attributed to Pythagoras, a
Greek of the sixth century BC, who gave his name to a sect called the
Pythagoreans. (Pythagoras' existence is disputed by many historians,
however.) The Pythagoreans believed that numbers and number
patterns were the key to understanding the world. However, it is clear
from clay tablets dating from about 2000 BC that early Babylonian
scribes knew about the theorem, and the result is also found in
ancient Chinese manuscripts. Pythagoras' Theorem is Proposition 47
of Book 1 of Euclid's *Elements*, and this is where the first rigorous
proof appears.

Pythagoras' Theorem is usually read as *Pythagoras's Theorem.*

Later in this subsection you will see why Pythagoras' Theorem is true. First we look at how it can be used to calculate the third side of a right-angled triangle when two sides are already known.

Example 11   *Using Pythagoras' Theorem to find the hypotenuse*

Calculate the length of the hypotenuse of the triangle below.

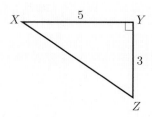

Solution

$\wp$ Relate the diagram to the statement of Pythagoras' Theorem. $\wp$

XZ is the hypotenuse and XY and YZ are the shorter sides.

$\wp$ Now use the theorem. $\wp$

By Pythagoras' Theorem,

$$XZ^2 = XY^2 + YZ^2.$$

Substituting in the lengths of the known sides gives

$$XZ^2 = 5^2 + 3^2 = 25 + 9 = 34.$$

This gives the length of the hypotenuse XZ as $\sqrt{34}$. (The alternative solution $-\sqrt{34}$ is rejected because lengths must be positive.)

In Example 11 the answer was given as a surd, $\sqrt{34}$. This is acceptable because the question is an abstract geometric problem. However, if the question were 'How far from your starting point would you be if you walked 3 metres north followed by 5 metres west?', then a decimal answer would be more appropriate. In this case the answer 'about 5.8 metres' would be sensible.

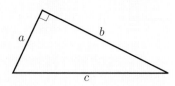

Figure 48   A right-angled triangle with shorter sides a and b, and hypotenuse c

Sometimes it is convenient to use Pythagoras' Theorem for a right-angled triangle with labelled sides rather than labelled vertices. For example, Pythagoras' Theorem applied to the right-angled triangle in Figure 48 gives

$$c^2 = a^2 + b^2.$$

When you know two side lengths of a right-angled triangle, they are not always the two sides adjacent to the right angle. The next example shows how to proceed in a case like this.

Example 12 *Using Pythagoras' Theorem to find a shorter side*

 Tutorial clip

Calculate the length of the third side of the triangle below.

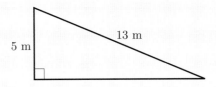

Solution

Let the length of the unknown side be b m. By Pythagoras' Theorem,

$$13^2 = 5^2 + b^2.$$

So

$$b^2 = 13^2 - 5^2 = 169 - 25 = 144.$$

Since b represents a length, we take the positive square root, which gives

$$b = \sqrt{144} = 12.$$

So the length of the third side is 12 m.

You can practise using Pythagoras' Theorem in the next activity.

Activity 27 *Using Pythagoras' Theorem*

Calculate the length of the third side of each of the following right-angled triangles. In part (d), give your answer to two decimal places.

(a)   (b)

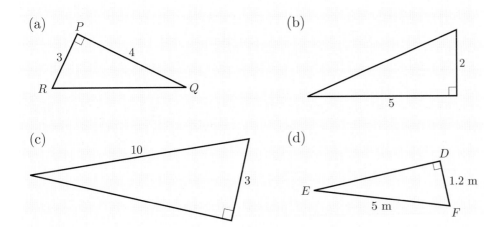

These diagrams are purposely not drawn to scale: this activity requires calculation rather than measurement.

(c)   (d)

In Activity 27(a) the right-angled triangle has whole-number lengths for the three sides, namely 3, 4 and 5. So

$$3^2 + 4^2 = 5^2.$$

Three whole numbers (like 3, 4 and 5) such that the square of one of them is equal to the sum of the squares of the other two are said to form a **Pythagorean triple**.

The Italian mathematician Leonardo Fibonacci (1170–1250) gave the following method for finding Pythagorean triples in one of his books.

Take any odd square number. Add up all the odd numbers that are smaller than this number; this will give another square number (you saw this fact in Unit 1). When you add the two square numbers together, you always get a third square number (this follows from the same fact in Unit 1). That is, you've found a Pythagorean triple.

There are other Pythagorean triples besides 3, 4, 5. For example, Example 12 shows that 5, 12, 13 is a Pythagorean triple. In fact, there are infinitely many Pythagorean triples – a method for calculating them is described in Euclid's *Elements*.

Pythagorean triples can be used to construct right angles, because the converse of Pythagoras' Theorem is true. It can be stated as follows.

If a triangle has sides of lengths a, b and c with $a^2 + b^2 = c^2$, then the angle opposite the side of length c is a right angle.

There is strong evidence that the 3, 4, 5 Pythagorean triple was known to the ancient Egyptians and Babylonians long before Pythagoras. There is also evidence that the ancient Egyptians knew that the converse of Pythagoras' Theorem is true and used it in practical situations to construct right angles; it is thought that they constructed 3, 4, 5 triangles using knots on a string in order to obtain accurate right angles.

There are many ways of proving Pythagoras' Theorem – the book *The Pythagorean Proposition* by E.S. Loomis (published in 1968) collects and classifies 370 proofs.

Now we move on from using Pythagoras' Theorem to the problem of showing why it is true. The video in the following activity demonstrates a visual proof of Pythagoras' Theorem.

Video

Activity 28   *Proof of Pythagoras' Theorem*

Watch the video *Proof of Pythagoras' Theorem*.

In addition to the visual proof shown in the video, there are more formal algebraic proofs. To end this section there follows an algebraic proof using the idea of similar triangles.

Proof of Pythagoras' Theorem

Consider the right-angled triangle shown in Figure 49.

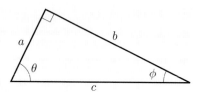

Figure 49   A right-angled triangle

Split the triangle by drawing a perpendicular from the vertex at the right angle. This gives the two triangles shown in Figure 50. The angles θ and ϕ are unchanged from Figure 49.

A **perpendicular** is a line at right angles to a given line.

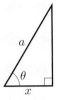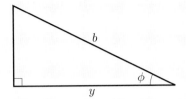

Figure 50 The triangle in Figure 49 split by the perpendicular from the right angle

The hypotenuse c has been split into two lengths x and y, so

$$c = x + y. \tag{3}$$

Now we express x and y in terms of the original lengths a, b and c.

First consider the left-hand triangle in Figure 50. Figure 51 shows this triangle flipped and rotated to be in the same orientation as the original triangle in Figure 49. It is similar to the original triangle (because they both have angles θ and $90°$). So the ratios of corresponding sides are equal. Hence

Figure 51 The left-hand triangle in Figure 50 flipped and rotated to be in the same orientation as the original triangle in Figure 49

$$\frac{x}{a} = \frac{a}{c}.$$

Multiplying both sides by a gives

$$x = \frac{a^2}{c}. \tag{4}$$

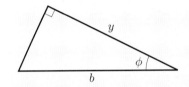

Now consider the right-hand triangle in Figure 50. Figure 52 shows this triangle flipped and rotated to be in the same orientation as the original triangle in Figure 49. This new triangle is also similar to the original triangle (because they both have angles ϕ and $90°$). Again the ratios of corresponding sides are equal, so

Figure 52 The right-hand triangle in Figure 50 flipped and rotated to be in the same orientation as the original triangle in Figure 49

$$\frac{y}{b} = \frac{b}{c}.$$

Multiplying both sides by b gives

$$y = \frac{b^2}{c}. \tag{5}$$

Using equations (4) and (5) to substitute into equation (3) gives

$$c = \frac{a^2}{c} + \frac{b^2}{c}.$$

Multiplying through by c gives

$$c^2 = a^2 + b^2.$$

This is Pythagoras' Theorem.

4 Perimeters and areas

A shape that can be drawn in a plane, such as the triangles and other polygons introduced in Section 2, is called a **plane shape**. This section considers two questions about plane shapes:

- What is the distance around the boundary of a shape – that is, what is its *perimeter*?

- How much surface does a shape occupy – that is, what is its *area*?

The section revises these properties for some basic shapes. It also discusses an application of these ideas: you will see how they can sometimes be used to determine whether cells in tissue samples are abnormal.

For help with areas and perimeters, see Maths Help Module 7, Section 3.

4.1 Finding perimeters and areas

The distance around the boundary of a shape is known as its **perimeter**. For example, Figure 53 shows a rectangle that is 2 cm by 3 cm. Its perimeter is

$$(3 + 2 + 3 + 2)\,\text{cm} = 10\,\text{cm}.$$

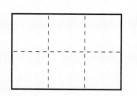

Figure 53 A rectangle cut into squares

The notion of **area** derives from the idea of counting how many squares of a standard size are needed to 'make' a shape. For example, the rectangle in Figure 53 can be cut into six squares, each with sides of length 1 cm, as shown. The area of each square is 1 *square* centimetre (written $1\,\text{cm}^2$). So the figure shows that the area of the 2 cm by 3 cm rectangle is

$$(2 \times 3)\,\text{cm}^2 = 6\,\text{cm}^2.$$

Similarly, Figure 54 shows an irregular shape whose area is approximately

$$\left(1 + 1 + \tfrac{1}{2} + \tfrac{1}{2}\right)\,\text{cm}^2 = 3\,\text{cm}^2.$$

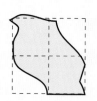

Figure 54 An irregular shape covering about two whole squares and two half-squares

If you wish to measure large areas, then square metres (m^2) or square kilometres (km^2) may be more appropriate units than square centimetres. For example, one square metre is the area of a square that is one metre by one metre.

You can convert between units of area by considering how many of the smaller units fit into one of the larger units. For example, a square of side 1 m contains $100 \times 100 = 10\,000$ squares of side 1 cm:

$$\begin{aligned}
1\,\text{m}^2 &= (1\,\text{m}) \times (1\,\text{m}) \\
&= (100\,\text{cm}) \times (100\,\text{cm}) \\
&= 10\,000\,\text{cm}^2.
\end{aligned}$$

So to convert a measurement in m^2 to cm^2, you multiply by 10 000. For example, an area of $0.5\,\text{m}^2$ is the same as

$$(0.5 \times 10\,000)\,\text{cm}^2 = 5000\,\text{cm}^2.$$

There are simple formulas for the areas of many standard shapes. The rectangle in Figure 53 illustrates the following formula.

The rectangle in Figure 53 has short sides of length 2 cm and long sides of length 3 cm, and its area is $(2 \times 3)\,\text{cm}^2 = 6\,\text{cm}^2$.

A rectangle with sides a and b has area ab.

When you use this formula, or any of the other formulas for area that you will meet in this subsection, you must be careful to use consistent units. For example, if a is in cm, then b must also be in cm, and the answer for the area will then be in cm^2.

The formula for the area of a rectangle can be used to find a formula for the area of a parallelogram. The **base** of a parallelogram can be taken to be any of its sides, and its **perpendicular height** is then its height measured at right angles to the base. The usual convention is to choose the 'bottom' side as the base. For example, the parallelogram in Figure 55 has base b and perpendicular height h.

In general, two lines are perpendicular if they meet or cross at right angles.

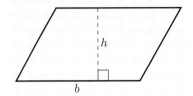

Figure 55 The base and perpendicular height of a parallelogram

Now consider splitting a parallelogram and reassembling it as shown in Figure 56. A right-angled triangle is cut from the right of the shape and attached to the left.

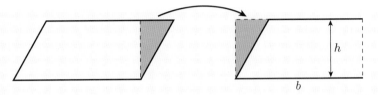

Figure 56 Splitting and reassembling a parallelogram

The triangle cut from the right of the parallelogram fits exactly on the left to form a rectangle, which gives the following formula.

> A parallelogram with base b and perpendicular height h has area bh.

This result can in turn be used to derive a formula for the area of a triangle, in terms of its base and perpendicular height. As for a parallelogram, the base of a triangle can be taken to be any of its sides, and its perpendicular height is then its height measured at right angles to the base, as shown in Figure 57.

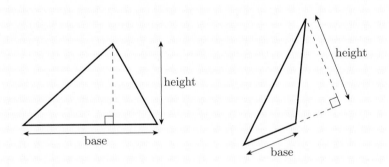

Figure 57 Base and height measurements of two triangles

Now consider making a copy of a triangle and rotating it through $180°$, as shown in Figure 58(a).

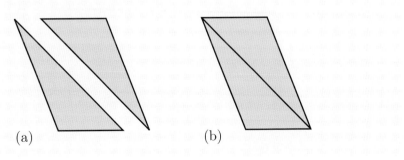

Figure 58 Putting together two copies of a triangle to form a parallelogram

Rotating a line through 180° leaves its direction unchanged, so each side of the original triangle is parallel to the corresponding side in the copy. So the triangle and the copy can be put together to form a parallelogram, as shown in Figure 58(b).

The area of the triangle is half of the area of the parallelogram, which gives the following formula.

The area of a triangle with base b and perpendicular height h is $\frac{1}{2}bh$.

The formulas in this subsection can be used to find not only the areas of the given shapes, but also the areas of shapes that are combinations of them, as the next example illustrates.

In this example no particular units are specified for the lengths of the sides of the shape.

Example 13 *Finding the area of an irregular shape*

Find the area of the trapezium shown below.

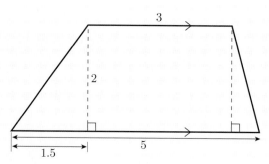

Solution

Split the shape into simpler shapes.

This shape is split by the dashed lines into a rectangle and two triangles.

Find the areas of the simpler shapes.

On the left is a triangle with base 1.5 and perpendicular height 2, which has area $\frac{1}{2} \times 1.5 \times 2 = 1.5$.

In the middle is a 3 by 2 rectangle, which has area $3 \times 2 = 6$.

On the right is a triangle with base $5 - 1.5 - 3 = 0.5$ and perpendicular height 2, which has area $\frac{1}{2} \times 0.5 \times 2 = 0.5$.

So the total area of the shape is $1.5 + 6 + 0.5 = 8$.

An alternative way to find the area of the trapezium in Example 13 is to split it into two triangles, as shown in Figure 59. Each triangle has height 2 units, and the bases are 5 units and 3 units. So the area of the trapezium is

$$\tfrac{1}{2} \times 5 \times 2 + \tfrac{1}{2} \times 3 \times 2 = 5 + 3 = 8.$$

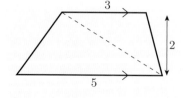

Figure 59   The trapezium in Example 13 split into two triangles

This method can be used for any trapezium, as illustrated in Figure 60.

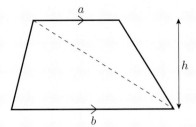

Figure 60   A trapezium split into two triangles

So the area of a trapezium with parallel sides a and b and perpendicular height h is given by the formula

$$\tfrac{1}{2}ah + \tfrac{1}{2}bh.$$

This expression can be simplified by taking out the common factor $\tfrac{1}{2}h$, which gives the formula below.

> The area of a trapezium with parallel sides a and b and perpendicular height h is $\tfrac{1}{2}(a+b)h$.

You can practise finding the areas of shapes in the following activity.

Activity 29   *Finding areas*

Find the areas of the following shapes. In part (d), give an answer in terms of x.

(a)

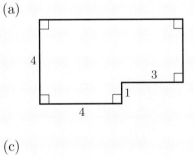

(b)

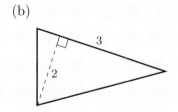

(c)

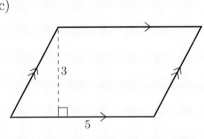

(d)

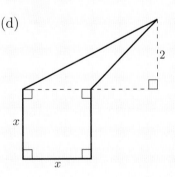

4.2   Using perimeters and areas

An interesting medical application of geometry is the detection of abnormal cells in the body. Traditional methods for detecting abnormality involve a trained technician using a microscope to identify and count abnormal cells in a tissue sample, which is a tiring task. Counting is an ideal task for a computer, but how should the computer decide which cells are abnormal?

One general feature of the type of abnormal cells shown in Figure 61 is that they have a more 'spiky' boundary. But how can a computer be programmed to recognise this property?

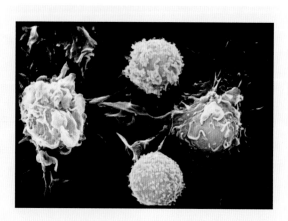

Figure 61   A photograph showing two normal cells (top and bottom) and two abnormal cells (left and right). The normal cells have much smoother surfaces.

Let's look at how the cells are presented to a computer. A microscope slide of cells is photographed to turn it into a computer image. A computer image is made up of *pixels*, which are small square regions of colour. Figure 62 illustrates this – it shows an image of two cells, a normal one on the left and an abnormal one on the right, with the size of the pixels exaggerated to make their square nature apparent.

The word 'pixel' comes from amalgamating the words *picture* and *element*.

Figure 62   Two cells seen as collections of pixels

The image in Figure 62 has also been 'thresholded'; that is, the interior of each cell has been coloured with a single colour, black, that is different from the colour of the surrounding area, which is beige. The question remains as to how a computer could classify the two cells in Figure 62 in terms of the spikiness of their boundaries.

In practice this is the most difficult step of the process: successfully differentiating cells from the surrounding fluid.

It's easy for a computer to calculate the perimeters of the two cells, simply by counting the number of units around the boundary. The two cells in Figure 62 have perimeters of 42 units and 62 units, respectively. So the abnormal cell has a larger perimeter: this corresponds to the intuitive notion that the boundary of an abnormal cell is more spiky than that of a normal cell. However, a normal cell that is larger than the cells in

Figure 62 will also tend to have a larger perimeter. For example, the image in Figure 63 is that of a normal cell, but its perimeter is 62 units, the same as that of the abnormal cell in Figure 62. So measuring the perimeter alone cannot distinguish between normal and abnormal cells.

This leads to the idea of dividing the perimeter of a cell by its area to compensate for the size of the cell. A computer can calculate the area of a cell by counting the number of black squares – both cells shown in Figure 62 have area 83 square units. Compensating for size in this way leads to the measure that this module will call **wiggliness**, which is defined as follows.

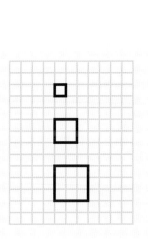

Figure 63   A larger normal cell

$$\text{wiggliness} = \frac{\text{perimeter}^2}{\text{area}}$$

You may wonder why the simpler formula

$$\text{wiggliness} = \frac{\text{perimeter}}{\text{area}}$$

isn't used – why should the perimeter be *squared* in the formula? To see why, consider what happens when a shape is enlarged, as in the following activity.

Activity 30   *Calculating the wiggliness of enlarged shapes*

Calculate the area, perimeter and wiggliness of each of the three shapes below; give the wiggliness to one decimal place.

(a)   (b)   (c)

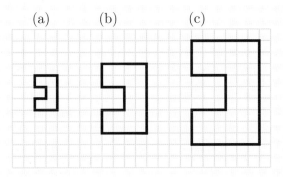

In this diagram each grid square has sides of length 1 unit.

The three shapes in Activity 30 are similar, with the second and third shapes enlarged compared to the first one. The scale factors of shapes (b) and (c) with respect to shape (a) are 2 and 3, respectively. When a shape is scaled, its perimeter, like all its lengths, is multiplied by the scale factor, so the perimeter of shape (b) is twice the perimeter of shape (a), and the perimeter of shape (c) is three times the perimeter of shape (a). However, the effect of scaling on its area is different. Figure 64 illustrates the effect of scaling on the area of a square whose sides are 1 unit long. If the length of the side is doubled, the area is four times as large, and if the side length is tripled, the area is nine times as large. In general, if the scale factor is k, then the area of the scaled square is k^2 times the area of the original square. Since the diagram in Activity 30 is made up of squares, the area of shape (b) is four times the area of shape (a), and the area of shape (c) is nine times the area of shape (a), as you can check from your solution.

Figure 64   Area scale factors

These effects of enlargement on perimeter and area hold for any shape. If a shape is scaled by the scale factor k, then its perimeter is multiplied by k and its area is multiplied by k^2.

Because of this, the wiggliness of a shape, as defined in the formula in the pink box, is unchanged as the shape is enlarged. To see this, consider a shape with perimeter P and area A. It has wiggliness P^2/A. Any scaled version of the shape has perimeter kP and area $k^2 A$ for some constant k, so it has wiggliness

$$\frac{(kP)^2}{k^2 A} = \frac{k^2 P^2}{k^2 A} = \frac{P^2}{A},$$

which is the same as for the original shape. This is precisely what we want: the wiggliness should be a property of the shape of an object that is independent of its size.

If the lengths are measured in metres, then the perimeter will also be measured in metres. So the perimeter squared will be measured in m², the same units as area. So the units will cancel, which means that 'wiggliness' is a number without units: its value is the same no matter what units are used to measure the lengths.

Wiggliness does not have any units associated with it: it is a 'pure number'. Such quantities are called **dimensionless quantities**, and they are often important in the investigation of real-world problems.

The next activity asks you to calculate the wiggliness of the three cell images in Figures 62 and 63.

Activity 31   *Calculating the wiggliness of cells*

(a) The large cell shown in Figure 63 has area 150 square units, so from the discussion above you now have the areas and perimeters of all three cells shown in Figures 62 and 63. Use this information to complete the following table; give the wiggliness to one decimal place.

Cell	Area	Perimeter	Wiggliness
Small normal			
Abnormal			
Large normal			

(b) Using the above table, suggest a criterion for determining whether a cell is abnormal.

4.3 Circles and π

Strictly, the circle is *just* the points on the boundary, and the 'filled-in' shape is called a *disc*. However, in this module we will use 'circle' to mean the whole shape.

The plural of radius is *radii*.

A **circle** is a shape whose boundary consists of all the points that are a fixed distance from a fixed point called the **centre** – to see that this is true, think about how you would draw a circle using a pair of compasses.

Special names are given to some parts of a circle, as illustrated in Figure 65. The boundary of a circle is called its **circumference**. A line segment from the centre to the circumference of a circle is called a **radius**. A line segment starting and ending on the circumference is called a **chord**. A chord that passes through the centre of the circle is called a **diameter**. Any unbroken section of the circumference is called an **arc**. The shape enclosed by an arc of a circle together with the two radii from the endpoints of the arc is called a **sector**. A **segment** is the shape enclosed by an arc and the chord joining the ends of the arc.

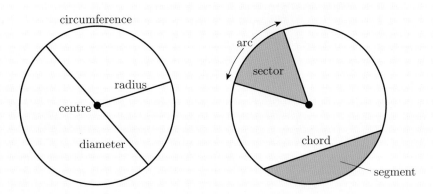

Figure 65 Parts of circles

The words circumference, radius and diameter are also used to refer to the *lengths* of these parts of a circle. For example, you can say that a circle has radius 2 cm.

The shape enclosed by a diameter of a circle, together with one of the two arcs from one end of the diameter to the other, is called a **semicircle** (Figure 66). Thus a semicircle is both a sector and a segment.

There is a well-known relationship between the circumference and radius of a circle:

> The circumference of a circle of radius r is $2\pi r$.

The number π is a constant that is one of the most remarkable numbers in mathematics, as it occurs frequently in many different contexts. It is a number that cannot be written down exactly as a terminating or recurring decimal – that is, it is irrational – so approximations to π are needed for practical applications. The value of π is 3.141 592 65 to eight decimal places.

There has been a lot of effort expended in calculating approximations to π.

In ancient times π was frequently taken to be 3, such as in the following Bible extract that describes the building of part of the temple of Solomon.

> Then he made the Sea of cast bronze, ten cubits from one brim to the other; it was completely round. Its height was five cubits, and a line of thirty cubits measured its circumference.
>
> (*New King James Bible*, II Chronicles 4:2)

From this quotation, the diameter of the object (equal to twice the radius) is ten cubits and the circumference is thirty cubits. Dividing the circumference by twice the radius gives the number that the author was using as an approximation to π, which is $30/10 = 3$, as stated above.

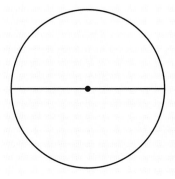

Figure 66 A diameter divides a circle into two semicircles

Unit 3 discussed the fact that every rational number has an expression as a terminating or recurring decimal.

The cubit is one of the earliest recorded units of length. Its length varied between different cultures – in Egypt, the royal cubit was about 52 cm.

Archimedes' dedication to geometry is suggested by the following quote.

'[Archimedes] ... being perpetually charmed by his familiar siren, that is, by his geometry, he neglected to eat and drink and took no care of his person; that he was often carried by force to the baths.'

Attributed to Plutarch, AD 46–120.

The fraction 22/7 was often used as an approximation to π before the widespread use of electronic calculators.

Another approximation by a fraction that is worth mentioning is 355/113, which was discovered by Chinese mathematician Zu Chongzhi in about AD 480. It is the closest approximation with the denominator below 1000, and is memorable because the sequence 113355 appears when you read it from bottom to top.

The Greek mathematician Archimedes (in approximately 240 BC) devised a method for calculating π to any desired accuracy. The method involves sandwiching a circle of radius 1, which has a circumference of 2π, between two regular polygons, as shown in Figure 67.

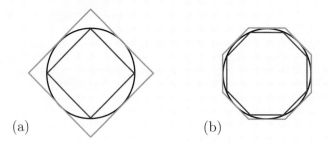

(a)   (b)

Figure 67   Approximating the circumference of a circle

Figure 67(a) shows a square **inscribed** in the circle, that is, drawn with corners touching the circle, and a larger square **circumscribed** outside the circle, that is, drawn with the centres of the sides touching the circle. Figure 67(b) shows the same circle, with inscribed and circumscribed octagons. The circumference of the circle is always sandwiched between the perimeters of the inscribed and circumscribed polygons. As the number of sides of the two polygons increases, the perimeters of the polygons provide closer approximations for the circumference of the circle. Since the exact circumference of the circle is 2π, dividing these approximations by 2 gives approximations for π. Archimedes used polygons with 96 sides to obtain $223/71 < \pi < 22/7$. This gives an approximation for π correct to two decimal places.

In the twentieth century, computer manufacturers used the calculation of π as a demonstration of the speed of their computers. As a result of this work, π has now been calculated to several billion decimal places. For practical purposes only a few decimal places are needed.

Most calculators have a button that gives an accurate approximation for π, and most mathematical software packages have a command that does this. In your calculations you should use these facilities rather than a simple approximation such as 22/7 or 3.14. For abstract problems it is usually best to avoid evaluating π at all and instead express answers in terms of π. For example, you might give the answers $\frac{3}{2}\pi$ or $\pi + 1$.

The following activity involves using the formula for the circumference of a circle.

Activity 32   *Estimating the length of the M25*

The M25 London orbital motorway is roughly circular with radius 25 km. Estimate the distance that a car travels as it circles London on the M25.

If you want to enclose a certain area of land with the shortest possible fence, then you should make your field circular. The circle is the shape that encloses the greatest possible area for a certain perimeter.

The constant π also appears in the formula for the area of a circle:

The area of a circle of radius r is πr^2.

This formula for the area of a circle has also been used to find approximations of π in the past, as the following activity shows.

Activity 33   *Estimating π from the Rhind papyrus*

The ancient Egyptian Rhind papyrus used the approximation that a circle of diameter 9 has the same area as a square of side 8. What value for π is given by this approximation?

The Rhind papyrus was mentioned in Unit 5.

The following example shows how the formula for the area of a circle can be used with other formulas to calculate the areas of more complicated shapes. This example also illustrates something that was mentioned in Unit 1 and which is often relevant to calculations involving areas of shapes: when you use intermediate results in later calculations, you should use the full-calculator-precision versions of the intermediate results, to avoid rounding errors.

For more examples on areas of circles, see Maths Help Module 7, Subsection 3.2.

Example 14   *Finding areas*

A gardener wishes to turf a rectangular lawn and wants to estimate how much turf she should buy. The lawn is six metres by ten metres and has a circular flower bed of radius two metres cut into it. If the turf comes in pieces that cover $1.5\,\text{m}^2$, how many pieces of turf should the gardener buy?

Solution

Collect the information in a diagram.

The essential information is usefully depicted as follows.

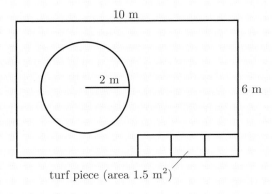

turf piece (area 1.5 m²)

Calculate the relevant areas and combine them.

The area of the large rectangle is

$$6\,\text{m} \times 10\,\text{m} = 60\,\text{m}^2.$$

The area of the circular flower bed is

$$\pi \times (2\,\text{m})^2 = 12.56\ldots\,\text{m}^2.$$

This gives the total area of lawn to be covered as

$$(60 - 12.56\ldots)\,\text{m}^2 = 47.43\ldots\,\text{m}^2.$$

So the number of pieces of turf required is

$$\frac{47.43\ldots}{1.5} = 31.62\ldots.$$

Subtracting one area from another to calculate the area of a shape with holes in it is a useful general strategy.

The gardener has to buy a whole number of pieces of turf, so she should buy 32 pieces and then cut some of these to fit around the circular flower bed.

Use the formula for the area of a circle to tackle the following problem.

Activity 34   *How much lawn seed?*

The gardener is now planning to seed a semicircular lawn of radius 3 m. The instructions on the box of seed say to scatter 50 g of seed for every square metre of lawn. How much lawn seed does the gardener need?

In this section, you have seen how to calculate the perimeters and areas of shapes composed of rectangles, triangles and circles. These types of calculations arise in many practical applications, such as estimating areas of land or calculating the quantities of materials needed for building or design projects.

5 Solids

Up until now, this unit has investigated plane shapes – shapes that can be drawn on a sheet of paper. Such shapes are said to be **two-dimensional** because they extend in two directions.

Geometry is not concerned only with two-dimensional shapes, but also with solid shapes such as spheres and cubes. These shapes, often known as **solids**, are said to be **three-dimensional** because they extend in three perpendicular directions. This short section introduces some three-dimensional shapes, and the related concepts of *volume* and *surface area*.

There are a number of words commonly used to describe the extent of a shape or an object in some direction; perhaps the five most familiar are length, breadth, width, height and depth. This section will primarily use the words width, height and depth, and will relate these to the way the shape or object is drawn in pictures as follows:

- *width* is the extent *across the page*
- *height* is the extent *up and down the page*
- *depth* is how far the object extends *into the page* (which is indicated by a perspective drawing).

5.1 Some standard solids

If you cut the solid in Figure 68 parallel to its ends, then the *cross-section* that you get always has the same shape and size as the ends. In other words, the cross-section is *uniform*. A solid with a uniform polygonal cross-section is called a **prism**. The prism in Figure 68 has a star-shaped cross-section, as shown.

A shape is *polygonal* if it is a polygon.

Another prism is shown in Figure 69: this one has a triangular cross-section, and a prism like this is called a **triangular prism**.

Figure 68   A star-shaped prism and a cross-section through it

A good way to think about a prism is to imagine filling in between two copies of a plane shape (the shape of the cross-section). In particular, a **cube** (Figure 70(a)) is an example of a prism, since it can be constructed by filling in between two copies of a square. (If the square has width and height a, then the two copies of the square must be distance a apart in order for the resulting solid to be a cube.) More generally, a **cuboid** (Figure 70(b)) – or more informally a box – is a prism whose cross-section is a rectangle. So a cube is a special case of a cuboid.

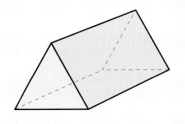

Figure 69   A triangular prism

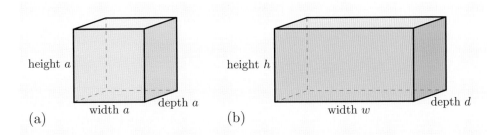

Figure 70   (a) A cube of width, height and depth a. (b) A cuboid of width w, height h and depth d.

Another important example of a solid with a uniform cross-section is a **cylinder** (Figure 71(a)), whose cross-section is a circle. (This solid isn't a prism because its cross-section isn't polygonal.) A cylinder is often drawn standing on one of its circular ends, so the distance between the two circles at its ends is usually denoted by h for height rather than d for depth.

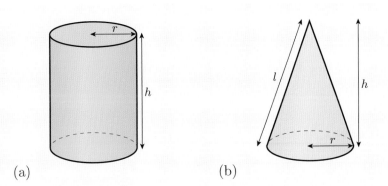

Figure 71   (a) A cylinder of radius r and height h. (b) A cone of height h whose base is a circle of radius r, with slant height l.

A related shape is a **cone** (Figure 71(b)), whose cross-sections are all circular but decrease in radius uniformly to a point, the **apex** of the cone. The **slant height** of a cone (denoted by l in Figure 71(b)) is the distance from the apex to any point on the circumference of the circular base.

In the prisms in Figures 68 and 69, each edge joining a vertex of one end of the prism to the matching vertex of the other end is perpendicular to the ends of the prism. Similarly, in the cylinder and cone in Figure 71, the line formed by the centres of the cross-sections is perpendicular to the base. In other texts you might see the words *prism*, *cylinder* and *cone* used to refer to solids in which these lines are not perpendicular to the base. Similarly, in other texts you might see the words *cylinder* and *cone* used to refer to solids with non-circular bases.

5.2 Volumes and surface areas of solids

Volumes

For more examples on volumes, see Maths Help Module 7, Subsection 3.4.

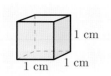

Figure 72   A cube with each edge of length 1 cm

A decimetre (dm) is one-tenth of a metre. Hence 1 dm = 10 cm and 1 dm^3 = 1000 cm^3.

The **volume** of a solid object is the amount of physical space that the object occupies. Volume can be measured in *cubic centimetres* (cm^3), or *cubic metres* (m^3), and so on. A cubic centimetre is the volume of a cube whose edges all have length 1 cm (Figure 72), and a cubic metre is the volume of a cube whose edges all have length 1 m, and so on. A cubic centimetre is sometimes abbreviated as cc rather than cm^3; for example, you might hear about a 50 cc moped engine.

The concept of volume is closely related to the concept of **capacity**, which is the amount of liquid that an object could contain. Some units of capacity are litres in the metric system, and pints and gallons in British Imperial units. One litre is the capacity of one cubic decimetre (dm^3).

There are simple formulas for the volumes of many standard solid shapes, just as there are for the areas of standard plane shapes. For example, the volume of a cuboid of width w, height h and depth d is obtained by multiplying the three measurements together, so the formula for the volume is whd.

Another way to think about this formula for the volume of a cuboid is as the area of a cross-section, wd, times the height, h. This works for any solid with a uniform cross-section: any prism, and also (for example) a cylinder. You can think of such a solid as a thickening of one of its cross-sections, the thickness being the height h. Using this notion, you can see that the volume is obtained by multiplying the area of the cross-section (denoted by A in this unit) by the height, h. This gives the formula Ah for the volume.

This derivation can be made more formal and rigorous, as you will see if you study higher-level mathematics modules.

In the particular case of a cylinder, the cross-section is a circle. If the radius is r, then the area A is πr^2, so the volume of the cylinder is $Ah = \pi r^2 h$.

The formulas found above, together with formulas for the volumes of more complex shapes, are collected together for convenience in Table 4 on the next page.

Surface areas

Informally, the **surface area** of a solid can be thought of as the area of paper needed to wrap the object without any overlapping. The units of surface area are the same as the units of area, for example cm^2 or m^2.

The surface area of a box of width w, height h and depth d can be found by adding together the areas of the six rectangles that are the faces of the box. In order to visualise these six rectangles, imagine cutting along some of the edges of the box and unfolding the rest. The result is known as a **net** of the box (see Figure 73).

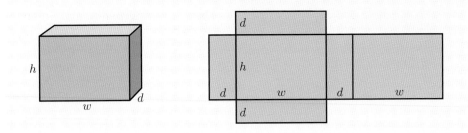

Figure 73   A box and a net of the box

Adding together the areas of the six faces gives the formula for the surface area as $2wh + 2wd + 2hd$.

Formulas for the surface areas of more complex shapes are given in Table 4, which collects together formulas for volumes and surface areas.

Table 4   Volumes and surface areas of simple solids

Shape	Diagram	Volume	Surface area
Cuboid		whd	$2wh + 2wd + 2hd$
Prism		Ah	$2A + hp$
Cylinder		$\pi r^2 h$	$2\pi r^2 + 2\pi rh$
Cone		$\frac{1}{3}\pi r^2 h$	$\pi r^2 + \pi rl$
Sphere		$\frac{4}{3}\pi r^3$	$4\pi r^2$

There is something worth noticing about the entries in Table 4. In each formula for surface area, each term is of the form

> constant × length × length   or   constant × area.

This is because in each case the unit needs to be a unit of area, such as m².

The sphere is the shape with minimum surface area for a certain volume. This is why soap bubbles in the air are spherical: the volume of air inside the bubble is fixed, and surface tension in the soap film acts to make the film have the smallest possible area. (You saw a similar result about the areas and circumferences of circles earlier.)

Similarly, in each formula for volume, each term is of the form

$$\text{constant} \times \text{length} \times \text{length} \times \text{length} \quad \text{or} \quad \text{constant} \times \text{area} \times \text{length}.$$

This is because in each case the unit needs to be a unit of volume, such as m^3. You can use these facts as a quick check on whether you have a correct formula. For example, if you are calculating a volume, then the formula should involve multiplying three lengths, or an area and a length, together.

5.3 Using volumes and surface areas

The following example shows how to apply one of the formulas in Table 4.

Example 15   *Finding the capacities of buckets*

A window cleaner has two cylindrical buckets, one with diameter 25 cm and height 30 cm, and the other with diameter 30 cm and height 25 cm. Which will hold more water?

Solution

The capacities of the buckets can be calculated by using the formula for the volume of a cylinder, $\pi r^2 h$. For the first bucket the height is $h = 30$ cm and the radius is $r = 25/2 = 12.5$ cm, which gives the volume in cm^3 as

$$\pi \times 12.5^2 \times 30 \approx 14\,726.$$

Since $1000\,cm^3$ is a litre, the capacity of the bucket is about 15 litres.

The second bucket has height $h = 25$ cm and radius $r = 30/2 = 15$ cm, so its volume in cm^3 is

$$\pi \times 15^2 \times 25 \approx 17\,671,$$

which represents a capacity of about 18 litres.

The capacity of the second bucket is larger, so it holds more water.

> If you want to make a bucket with a certain volume, but using the smallest area of sheet material, then you should make the diameter of the bucket equal to twice its height. Real buckets are not this optimal shape, probably because such a wide bucket would be hard to carry.
>
> On the other hand, if you want a bucket with a lid, you can enclose the greatest volume with the smallest amount of material if you make the height and diameter of the cylinder equal. It's probably no coincidence that paint tins often have roughly these proportions.

Activity 35   *Finding the surface area of a metal can*

What is the surface area of a metal can that is a cylinder of diameter 7.5 cm and height 10.5 cm?

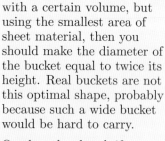

Figure 74   A hemisphere of radius r

Here are two final activities for you to try. They involve a solid called a *hemisphere*, which means half a sphere, as shown in Figure 74. More precisely, a **hemisphere** is the solid shape obtained by cutting a sphere along a plane through its centre.

Activity 36   *How much foil?*

A dome is to be constructed out of steel and transparent foil in a similar way to the greenhouses shown in Figure 75. Model the dome as a hemisphere of radius 10 m to calculate the area of foil required to construct the dome to the nearest ten square metres.

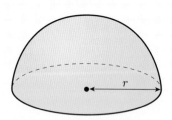

Figure 75   Greenhouses at the Eden Project in Cornwall

Activity 37 *How many ice cream cones?*

This question concerns ice cream cones of diameter 6 cm and height 12 cm, filled with ice cream all the way to the bottom of the cone and heaped on top in such a way that the upper surface is a hemisphere.

(a) Calculate the volume of ice cream needed to make an ice cream cone to the above description. Give your answer in cubic centimetres rounded to the nearest cubic centimetre.

(b) Convert the volume of ice cream found in part (a) to litres.

(c) Hence calculate the number of ice cream cones of the above description that could be made from a one-litre tub of ice cream.

Many modern buildings use geometric properties of solid shapes in innovative ways. One of the most famous is the Sydney Opera House, shown in Figure 76. The curved surfaces are parts of spheres, all with the same radius.

Figure 76 Sydney Opera House

This unit has introduced the basics of geometry. In Unit 12 you will see how to calculate the areas of more complicated shapes, but there are many other important and useful areas of geometry, which you may encounter if you continue with further study in mathematics. For example, you could learn about the perspective that artists use to represent three-dimensional objects on a two-dimensional canvas (this is called *projective geometry*), or you could study the geometry of regular patterns such as tiling patterns, and their rotational and mirror symmetries, which are considerably more varied than the symmetries that you have seen in this unit.

Learning checklist

After studying this unit, you should be able to:

- determine angles in shapes using the following facts:
  - the angles in a triangle add up to 180°
  - the angles on a straight line add up to 180°
  - the angles making up a right angle add up to 90°
  - when two lines cross, the opposite (X) angles are equal
  - when a line crosses two parallel lines, the corresponding (F) angles are equal
  - when a line crosses two parallel lines, the alternate (Z) angles are equal
- construct geometric arguments
- identify line and rotational symmetries
- show that two triangles are congruent
- calculate the lengths of corresponding sides in similar triangles
- use Pythagoras' Theorem to calculate the length of a side of a right-angled triangle when given the other two lengths
- calculate the areas and perimeters of some shapes constructed from rectangles, triangles and parts of circles
- calculate the volumes and surface areas of simple solids.

Solutions and comments on Activities

Activity 2

(a) BCD is a straight line. So

$\alpha + 50° = 180°$ (angles on a straight line)

$\alpha = 180° - 50° = 130°$.

(b) $\angle ACB$ and $\angle DCE$ are obtuse.

(c)

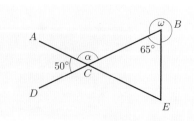

The angles in a full turn add up to 360°. So

$\omega = 360° - 65° = 295°$.

Activity 3

Angles on a straight line add up to 180°. So

$2\theta + 110° = 180°$

$2\theta = 70°$

$\theta = 35°$.

Activity 4

(a) The marked angles are always equal.

(b) The alternate angles α and γ are equal. See the comments in the text panel in the dynamic geometry resource.

Activity 5

(a) $\theta + \psi = 180°$ (angles on a straight line).

(b) $\psi + \phi = 180°$ (angles on a straight line).

(c) Subtracting the equation in part (b) from the equation in part (a) gives

$\theta - \phi = 0°$.

Hence $\theta = \phi$.

(You might have eliminated ψ in a different way.)

Activity 6

Since $\angle ABC$ and $\angle HBE$ are opposite angles, $\angle HBE = 40°$.

Also, $\angle FAD$ is opposite to $\angle BAC$, so $\angle FAD = 70°$.

Finally, FAC is a straight line, so $\angle BAF = 180° - 70° = 110°$.

Activity 7

$\angle BEF$ is opposite $\angle DEG$ and is therefore also equal to 50°.

$\angle ABE$ is an alternate angle with $\angle BEF$ (and also a corresponding angle with $\angle DEG$), and so is equal to 50°.

Finally, $\angle HBC$ is opposite $\angle ABE$ (and also a corresponding angle with $\angle BEF$), and so is also equal to 50°.

Activity 8

The three angles marked θ are angles on a straight line and hence add to 180°. Thus

$3\theta = 180°$

$\theta = 60°$.

So

$\angle ABE = 2 \times 60° = 120°$.

$\angle ABE$ and the angle marked ϕ are alternate angles, so

$\phi = 120°$.

Activity 9

Follow the instructions in the text panel of the 'Triangle' tab in the dynamic geometry resource to see how the result about the angles in a triangle can be proved.

Activity 10

The three angles of a triangle add up to 180°. In an equilateral triangle these angles are also equal, so each of the angles is $\frac{180}{3} = 60°$.

Activity 11

To find the required angles, use the fact that the angles of a triangle add up to 180°.

(a) The two base angles are equal to 62°. Let θ be the apex angle. Then

$\theta + 62° + 62° = 180°$

$\theta = 180° - 124°$

$\theta = 56°$.

So the apex angle is 56°.

(b) Let θ be the size of each base angle of the isosceles triangle with apex angle 30°. Then

$\theta + \theta + 30° = 180°$

$2\theta = 150°$

$\theta = 75°$.

So the base angles are each 75°.

Activity 12

Each of the matching wooden strips makes an angle of 65° with the vertical. Thus $\angle DKH = 65°$. Since $\angle DKH$ and $\angle HKC$ are angles on a straight line, they add to 180°. Therefore

$$\angle HKC = 180° - 65° = 115°.$$

Similarly, $\angle LJI = 65°$, and so $\angle CJI = 115°$. There are at least two ways to find $\angle KCJ$. One way is to note that $\angle HKC$ and $\angle KCB$ are alternate angles, as are $\angle IJC$ and $\angle JCB$. Thus both $\angle KCB$ and $\angle JCB$ are equal to 115°. Therefore

$$\angle KCJ = 360° - 2 \times 115° = 130°.$$

Another way is to extend the line BC, say to M.

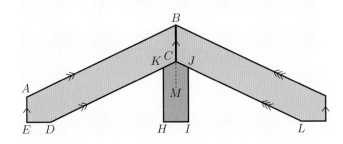

Now, since the matching strips each make an angle of 65° with the vertical, it follows that
$\angle KCM = \angle MCJ = 65°$.
Since $\angle KCJ = \angle KCM + \angle MCJ$, it follows that

$$\angle KCJ = 2 \times 65° = 130°.$$

Activity 13

(a) Using the fact that the angles in a triangle add up to 180° gives

$$\angle CBD = 180° - 30° - \theta = 150° - \theta.$$

But AD is a straight line, so
$\angle ABC + \angle CBD = 180°$, which gives

$$\begin{aligned}
\angle ABC &= 180° - \angle CBD \\
&= 180° - (150° - \theta) \\
&= 180° - 150° + \theta \\
&= 30° + \theta.
\end{aligned}$$

(b) Using the fact that the angles in a triangle add up to 180° gives $\angle ABD = 180° - 90° - \theta$, which simplifies to

$$\angle ABD = 90° - \theta.$$

Now $\angle ABC$, $\angle ABD$ and $\angle DBE$ add to 180° as they are angles on the straight line EC. Since $\angle DBE$ is 90°, and we have just found that $\angle ABD = 90° - \theta$, this gives the equation

$$\angle ABC + (90° - \theta) + 90° = 180°.$$

So

$$\begin{aligned}
\angle ABC - \theta &= 0° \\
\angle ABC &= \theta.
\end{aligned}$$

Activity 14

The conjecture is that the sum of the exterior angles of a triangle add up to 360°.

Each exterior angle of the triangle is on a straight line with the corresponding interior angle of the triangle. Therefore if the exterior angles are α, β and γ, then the interior angles are $180° - \alpha$, $180° - \beta$ and $180° - \gamma$.

From the result that the interior angles of a triangle add up to 180°, it follows that

$$\begin{aligned}
(180° - \alpha) + (180° - \beta) + (180° - \gamma) &= 180° \\
540° - (\alpha + \beta + \gamma) &= 180° \\
540° - 180° &= \alpha + \beta + \gamma \\
\alpha + \beta + \gamma &= 360°.
\end{aligned}$$

This proves the conjecture.

Activity 15

Read the discussion in the 'Parallelogram' tab of the dynamic geometry resource – this demonstrates that opposite angles of a parallelogram are equal.

Activity 16

A hexagon divided into triangles is shown below.

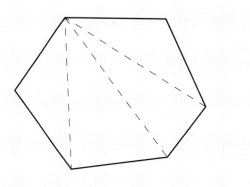

From the figure you can see that the hexagon has been split into four triangles, and each angle in each triangle is an angle in the hexagon or a part of one of these angles. So the angle sum of a hexagon is $4 \times 180° = 720°$.

(You may have split up your hexagon differently; there are several ways to do it, but they all give four triangles.)

Activity 17

The solution to Activity 16 shows that the angle sum of a hexagon is 720°. Since there are six equal interior angles in a regular hexagon, each angle is

$$\frac{720°}{6} = 120°.$$

Activity 18

(a) Since AE and BE represent equal lengths of rope, $\triangle ABE$ is an isosceles triangle. So its base angles, $\angle ABE$ and $\angle BAE$, are equal.

Similarly, $\triangle BCE$ is an isosceles triangle. So its base angles, $\angle EBC$ and $\angle ECB$, are equal.

(b) In the diagram below, $\angle ABE$ is labelled as α.

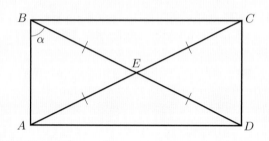

(i) $\angle BAE = \alpha$.

(ii) Since the interior angles of a triangle add up to $180°$,
$$\angle AEB = 180° - \alpha - \alpha = 180° - 2\alpha.$$

(iii) Since angles on a straight line add up to $180°$,
$$\begin{aligned}
\angle BEC &= 180° - \angle AEB \\
&= 180° - (180° - 2\alpha) \\
&= 180° - 180° + 2\alpha \\
&= 2\alpha.
\end{aligned}$$

(iv) Since the interior angles of a triangle add up to $180°$,
$$\angle EBC + \angle ECB + \angle BEC = 180°;$$
that is,
$$\angle EBC + \angle ECB + 2\alpha = 180°.$$
So
$$\angle EBC + \angle ECB = 180° - 2\alpha.$$
Since $\angle EBC = \angle ECB$ (from part (a)), it follows that
$$2 \times \angle EBC = 180° - 2\alpha,$$
so
$$\angle EBC = 90° - \alpha.$$

(c) Hence
$$\angle ABE + \angle EBC = \alpha + (90° - \alpha) = 90°.$$
So $\angle ABC$, which is $\angle ABE + \angle EBC$, is a right angle.

(d) Since all the angles are $90°$, $ABCD$ is a rectangle.

Activity 19

(a) This is a regular octagon, so it has rotational symmetry of order 8 (the number of sides).

(b) The letter 'S' has rotational symmetry of order 2.

(c) This picture can be rotated 8 times around the centre before returning to its starting point and each time the picture will look the same, so the order of rotational symmetry is 8.

(d) Each of the five depressed sections in the wheel can be rotated to the next, so the order of rotational symmetry is 5. (This ignores the faint logo at the centre of the wheel.)

Activity 20

(a) A square has four lines of symmetry.

(b) A rectangle has two lines of symmetry.

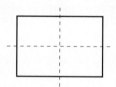

(c) A parallelogram has no lines of symmetry. (It does, however, have rotational symmetry of order 2.)

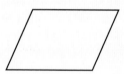

(d) A kite has just one line of symmetry.

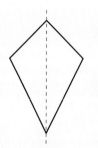

Activity 21

(a) Each triangle has sides of lengths 3, 4 and 6. So the two triangles are congruent by SSS.

(b) In this case we are given two pairs of sides equal and the included angles equal, so the two triangles are congruent by SAS.

(c) The three angles are the same in both triangles. However, although each triangle has a side of length 2, these sides are not corresponding. So the triangles are different sizes and hence are not congruent.

(d) Two angles in one triangle are equal to two angles in the other triangle, so the remaining angles in the triangles are also equal. However, the two triangles may be different sizes, so they are not necessarily congruent.

Activity 22

First notice that $\angle DCE = 50°$, since it is opposite to $\angle ACB$ at vertex C.

In $\triangle ABC$ and $\triangle DEC$:

- $AC = DC$
- $\angle ACB = \angle DCE$ (both angles are 50°)
- $BC = EC$.

So $\triangle ABC \cong \triangle DEC$ (by SAS).

Activity 23

(a) First notice that $\angle DCE = \theta$ since it is opposite to $\angle ACF$ at vertex C.

In $\triangle BCE$ and $\triangle DCE$:

- $\angle BCE = \angle DCE$ (both angles are θ)
- the side CE is common to both triangles
- $\angle BEC = \angle DEC$ (both angles are 90°).

So $\triangle BCE \cong \triangle DCE$ (by ASA).

(b) The line segments BE and DE are corresponding sides in congruent triangles (since they are both opposite to the angle θ), so they are equal.

Activity 24

$\triangle LMN$, $\triangle RST$ and $\triangle XYZ$ are similar because these triangles have the same three angles as each other. So the ratios of corresponding sides are equal. First consider $\triangle LMN$ and $\triangle RST$. The sides MN and ST are corresponding since they are both opposite the angle marked with one arc. Similarly, NL and TR are corresponding, and ML and SR are also corresponding. So

$$\frac{ST}{MN} = \frac{TR}{NL} = \frac{SR}{ML}.$$

Substituting in the known lengths gives

$$\frac{ST}{5} = \frac{10}{8} = \frac{SR}{10}.$$

So

$$ST = \frac{5 \times 10}{8} = \frac{50}{8} = 6.25$$

and

$$SR = \frac{10 \times 10}{8} = \frac{100}{8} = 12.5.$$

Now consider $\triangle XYZ$ and $\triangle LMN$. This gives

$$\frac{XZ}{8} = \frac{20}{5} = \frac{YX}{10}.$$

So

$$XZ = \frac{20 \times 8}{5} = 32,$$

and

$$YX = \frac{20 \times 10}{5} = 40.$$

Activity 25

(a) The Sun's rays are parallel, so we have the following diagram.

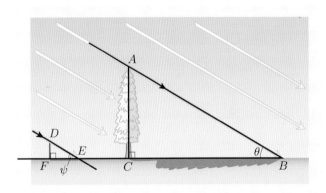

The angles θ and ψ are equal because they are a pair of corresponding (F) angles. Also, each of the two triangles contains a right angle. So two angles in one triangle are equal to two angles in the other triangle. Therefore $\triangle ABC$ is similar to $\triangle DEF$.

(b) Since $\triangle ABC$ is similar to $\triangle DEF$, the ratios of corresponding sides are equal, so

$$\frac{AC}{DF} = \frac{BC}{EF}.$$

Now $BC = 32.5$, $EF = 1.6$ and $DF = 1$, where all measurements are in metres.

Hence

$$\frac{AC}{1} = \frac{32.5}{1.6},$$

so
$$AC = \frac{32.5}{1.6} \approx 20.3.$$

Hence the height of the tree is approximately 20.3 metres.

Activity 26

(a) These two triangles are not similar. The ratio of the shortest side of the second triangle to the shortest side of the first is $2:1$, since $4 = 2 \times 2$, so if these triangles were similar, the scale factor would be $k = 2$. But the other two pairs of sides are not in the ratio $2:1$, so they don't correspond to $k = 2$.

(b) Since the angles in a triangle add up to $180°$, each triangle has angles of $100°$, $50°$ and $30°$. So the angles are the same and hence the triangles are similar.

(c) Here two pairs of sides have the same ratio, namely $k = 2$, since $5 = 2 \times 2.5$ and $6 = 2 \times 3$. However, the marked angle is not included, and it is possible to draw two triangles with these dimensions that are not similar. For example,

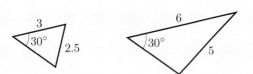

(d) Here two pairs of sides have the same ratio and there is an included angle, so the triangles are similar.

Activity 27

(a) By Pythagoras' Theorem,
$$RQ^2 = PR^2 + PQ^2 = 3^2 + 4^2 = 25.$$
So
$$RQ = \sqrt{25} = 5.$$
(The negative square root is disregarded as lengths are positive.)

(b) Let the length of the unknown side be c. By Pythagoras' Theorem,
$$c^2 = 2^2 + 5^2 = 29.$$
So $c = \sqrt{29}$.

(As the problem is abstract, it is not necessary to calculate a decimal approximation such as $\sqrt{29} \approx 5.39$.)

(c) Let the length of the unknown side be b. By Pythagoras' Theorem,
$$3^2 + b^2 = 10^2,$$
that is,
$$9 + b^2 = 100,$$
thus
$$b^2 = 91.$$
So $b = \sqrt{91}$.

(d) By Pythagoras' Theorem,
$$EF^2 = ED^2 + DF^2.$$
Substituting $DF = 1.2$ and $EF = 5$ gives
$$5^2 = ED^2 + 1.2^2.$$
So
$$ED^2 = 5^2 - 1.2^2 = 25 - 1.44 = 23.56.$$
Hence
$$ED = \sqrt{23.56} \approx 4.85.$$

That is, the length of the third side is approximately 4.85 m.

(Here the answer is calculated as a decimal value, since the problem is a practical one involving lengths with units.)

Activity 29

(a) The shape can be split into two rectangles in different ways. For example, consider the following split.

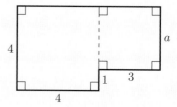

The next step is to calculate the length a in the diagram. This can be done by looking at the lengths of the other vertical sides, which gives
$$a = 4 - 1 = 3.$$
So the area of the shape is
$$4 \times 4 + 3 \times 3 = 16 + 9 = 25.$$

(An alternative way to calculate the area is to think of the shape as the difference between two rectangles, as follows.

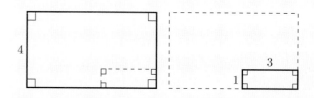

The width of the larger rectangle is $4 + 3 = 7$, so the area of the shape is
$$4 \times 7 - 1 \times 3 = 28 - 3 = 25,$$
as found previously.)

(b) The area of this triangle can be calculated directly by using the formula $\frac{1}{2}bh$. The base of the triangle can be taken to be the uppermost side. Then the base, b, is 3 and the perpendicular height, h, is 2, so the area of the triangle is
$$\tfrac{1}{2}bh = \tfrac{1}{2} \times 3 \times 2 = 3.$$

(c) Using the formula for the area of a parallelogram of base 5 and perpendicular height 3 gives the area as $5 \times 3 = 15$.

(d)

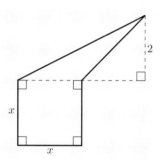

This shape splits up into a square with sides x and a triangle with base x and perpendicular height 2. The area of a square with sides x is $x \times x = x^2$. The area of a triangle with base x and perpendicular height 2 is $\frac{1}{2} \times x \times 2 = x$. So the area of the shape is $x^2 + x$.

(The expression $x^2 + x$ is an example of a *quadratic expression*, so this shows how such expressions arise naturally when calculating the areas of shapes with sides of unknown length. You will learn about quadratic expressions in Units 9 and 10.)

Activity 30

The answers are in the table below.

	Area	Perimeter	Wiggliness
(a)	5	12	$\dfrac{144}{5} = 28.8$
(b)	20	24	$\dfrac{24^2}{20} = 28.8$
(c)	45	36	$\dfrac{36^2}{45} = 28.8$

(You can see that the wiggliness of the shape is unchanged by enlargements with scale factor 2 or 3. This outcome is discussed in the text following the activity.)

Activity 31

(a) Your completed table should be as follows.

Cell	Area	Perimeter	Wiggliness
Small normal	83	42	21.3
Abnormal	83	62	46.3
Large normal	150	62	25.6

(b) Based on the table, a threshold of between 30 and 40, say, might be appropriate to distinguish the two types of cells. For example, the criterion might be that cells with a wiggliness less than 35 are classified as normal, while those with a wiggliness greater than 35 are classed as abnormal.

(Much more data would need to be collected before a more precise threshold could be defined. A trial that compared the calculated wiggliness of cells against human judgement of abnormality could provide these data.)

Activity 32

The radius of the motorway is 25 km. So the circumference is
$$2 \times \pi \times 25 \,\mathrm{km} \approx 157.080 \,\mathrm{km}.$$
It would be ridiculous to quote the answer to this precision, since the motorway is only approximately circular and the given radius, 25 km, is also approximate. Rounding to the nearest 10 km seems sensible, so an appropriate answer is that a car travels about 160 km.

(This rough calculation compares moderately well with the actual length of the M25, which is 188.3 km.)

Activity 33

A square of side 8 has area $8 \times 8 = 64$. A circle of diameter 9 has radius 4.5 and hence area $\pi \times 4.5^2$. Assuming that the square and circle have the same area gives the equation
$$64 = \pi \times 4.5^2.$$
Making π the subject of this equation gives
$$\pi = \frac{64}{4.5^2} \approx 3.16.$$

So the approximation for π implicit in this part of the Rhind papyrus is
$$\pi \approx 3.16.$$

(This approximation is quite close to the true value; it is accurate to within 1%.)

Activity 34

The area of a semicircle of radius r is $\frac{1}{2}\pi r^2$. If the radius is 3 m, then the area in m^2 is

$$\frac{1}{2} \times \pi \times 3^2 = \frac{9\pi}{2}.$$

So the amount of grass seed needed in grams is

$$\frac{9\pi}{2} \times 50 = 700 \text{ (to 1 s.f.)}.$$

Hence approximately 0.7 kg of seed is needed.

Activity 35

The surface area A of a cylinder of radius r and height h is given by the formula

$$A = 2\pi r^2 + 2\pi r h.$$

The diameter of the can is 7.5 cm, so the radius is 3.75 cm.

Substituting $r = 3.75$ and $h = 10.5$ into the formula gives

$$A = 2 \times \pi \times (3.75)^2 + 2 \times \pi \times 3.75 \times 10.5$$
$$\approx 335.75\ldots.$$

So the surface area of the can is approximately 340 cm^2.

Activity 36

The area of foil required is half of the surface area of a sphere of radius 10 m. The surface area of a sphere of radius r is given by the formula $4\pi r^2$, so the area, in m^2, of foil required for the dome is

$$\frac{1}{2} \times 4 \times \pi \times 10^2 \approx 628.31\ldots.$$

So, to the nearest ten square metres, the dome will require 630 m^2 of foil.

Activity 37

(a) The first step is to draw a diagram and add all relevant information. For this question you don't need to draw a three-dimensional shape: you can write all the relevant information on a diagram of a cross-section of the shape, as shown below.

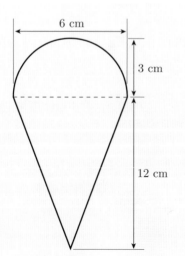

This shape splits into upper and lower parts as indicated by the dashed line in the diagram.

The lower part of the shape is a cone, so its volume is given by the formula $\frac{1}{3}\pi r^2 h$. The radius r is 3 cm and the height h is 12 cm, so the volume in cm^3 is

$$\frac{1}{3} \times \pi \times 3^2 \times 12 = 113.09\ldots.$$

The upper part of the shape is half of a sphere. The volume of a sphere of radius r is given by the formula $\frac{4}{3}\pi r^3$, so the volume, in cm^3, of the upper part is

$$\frac{1}{2} \times \frac{4}{3} \times \pi \times 3^3 = 56.54\ldots.$$

So the total volume in cm^3 of the ice cream is

$$113.09\ldots + 56.54\ldots = 169.64\ldots.$$

To the nearest cubic centimetre the volume is 170 cm^3.

(b) There are 1000 cm^3 in one litre. So the number of litres of ice cream in one cone is

$$\frac{169.64\ldots}{1000} = 0.169\ldots,$$

that is, each ice cream cone is made from approximately 0.17 litres of ice cream.

(c) The number of ice cream cones that can be made can be found by dividing the amount of ice cream in the tub by the amount of ice cream required to make one cone:

$$\text{number of cones} = \frac{1}{0.169\ldots} = 5.894\ldots.$$

So the one-litre tub of ice cream will make 5 full ice cream cones (with enough left over to make 89% of another cone).

Expanding algebra

Introduction

So far in the module you have used algebra in a variety of different situations. For example, in Units 6 and 7 you saw how linear models can be used to describe different practical situations, and in Unit 8 you saw how Pythagoras' Theorem together with algebraic manipulations helps to solve various geometric problems. However, many problems in science, technology and other fields lead to more complicated algebra, involving *quadratic expressions*, *algebraic fractions* and *powers*.

In this unit, you will develop further algebraic skills so that you can rearrange more complicated formulas and solve a greater range of equations. In particular, you will learn how to use a formula to obtain the sum of the terms of any *arithmetic sequence* such as

$$3, 7, 11, \ldots, 35,$$

and how to solve *quadratic equations* such as

$$3x^2 + 7x + 4 = 0,$$

by the method of factorisation. You will meet other ways to solve quadratic equations in Unit 10 and also see there how they can be used to solve practical problems involving objects in motion.

There are also many tutorial clips on algebraic techniques, and you are recommended to view them to help you understand the techniques.

This unit contains a large number of examples and activities on basic algebraic techniques. These have been included to give you the opportunity to develop skills that are important for studying further mathematics modules, so try to work through as many as you can.

1   Number patterns and algebra

1.1   Arithmetic sequences

Gauss is considered to be one of the greatest mathematicians of all time. His method of solving linear equations was mentioned in Unit 7, Section 3.

There is a story that the mathematician Carl Friedrich Gauss, when he was 10 years old, surprised his teacher by adding up the natural numbers from 1 to 100 very quickly, giving the answer 5050. The young Gauss is said to have noticed the following efficient way to do this addition.

You can rewrite the sum by rearranging it as a sum of pairs of numbers:

Remember that '...' means that something has been left out; it is read as 'dot, dot, dot'.

$$1 + 2 + \cdots + 99 + 100 = (1 + 100) + (2 + 99) + \cdots + (50 + 51).$$

There are 50 pairs of numbers in brackets, and each pair has sum 101, so

$$1 + 2 + \cdots + 99 + 100 = 50 \times 101 = 5050.$$

Activity 1   *Adding up numbers*

Use the method above to add up the natural numbers from 1 to 200.

What happens if you add up odd numbers? In Section 4 of Unit 1 you were asked to add up the odd numbers

$$1, 3, 5, 7, \ldots,$$

in longer and longer groups, as in the following table.

How many odd numbers	Sum
1	$1 = 1$
2	$1 + 3 = 4$
3	$1 + 3 + 5 = 9$
4	$1 + 3 + 5 + 7 = 16$

On the basis of these examples it appears that if you add up successive odd numbers starting with 1, then the answer is always the square of how many odd numbers you add. For example, in the last line of the table, the first four odd numbers are added and their sum is 16, which is 4^2. This observation led to the following neat formula.

The sum of the first n odd numbers is n^2.

Since there is a formula for the sum of the first n odd numbers, it is reasonable to ask if there is a formula for the sum of the first n natural numbers. Let's look at a table of the first few such sums.

Remember that the natural numbers are
$$1, 2, 3, \ldots.$$

How many numbers	Sum
1	$1 = 1$
2	$1 + 2 = 3$
3	$1 + 2 + 3 = 6$
4	$1 + 2 + 3 + 4 = 10$

In this case a pattern for the sums is not so clear. Figure 1 shows a geometric interpretation of these numbers. You can see that for the first four values of n, the sum of the natural numbers from 1 to n can be represented by a triangular arrangement of dots.

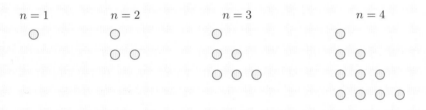

Figure 1   Triangles of dots

It is still not clear from these triangles whether there is a concise formula for the number of dots in the nth triangle. However, by drawing a rotated copy of each of these triangles next to itself, you can obtain rectangles of dots, as shown in Figure 2.

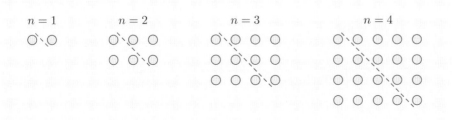

Figure 2   Rectangles of dots

The numbers of dots in these rectangles are

$$1 \times 2 = 2, \quad 2 \times 3 = 6, \quad 3 \times 4 = 12, \quad 4 \times 5 = 20, \quad \ldots.$$

From this construction, you can see that the rectangle constructed from the nth triangle of dots has n rows each with $n+1$ dots, making $n(n+1)$ dots in all. Hence the original triangle must have *half* this many dots, that is, $\frac{1}{2}n(n+1)$ dots. Since the nth triangle has $1 + 2 + \cdots + n$ dots, this gives the formula

$$1 + 2 + \cdots + n = \tfrac{1}{2}n(n+1).$$

The first few values of the expression $\frac{1}{2}n(n+1)$ are shown in the table below.

n	1	2	3	4	5	6	7
$\frac{1}{2}n(n+1)$	1	3	6	10	15	21	28

The numbers given by the expression $\frac{1}{2}n(n+1)$ are called **triangular numbers** since they occur as the numbers of dots in the triangular arrays illustrated in Figure 1. These numbers appear in a practical situation as the numbers of pills that can be easily counted in a triangular pill tray. The triangular tray shown in Figure 3 is used because, as pills are put in it, they form a stable triangular pattern. So to count them the pharmacist just needs to check how many rows of pills there are and then read off the corresponding triangular number from a table of these numbers.

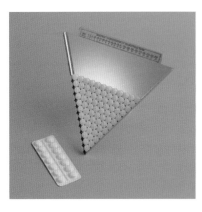

Figure 3 A triangular pill tray

You have seen a geometric proof of the formula for the sum of the first n natural numbers. Another way to prove it is to use an algebraic method based on the pairing method of Gauss. As preparation for this proof, here is a slightly different way to write down Gauss' method for adding the first 100 natural numbers.

First, let S denote the sum that you want to find:

$$S = 1 + 2 + \cdots + 99 + 100.$$

Then rearrange the sum in reverse order:

$$S = 100 + 99 + \cdots + 2 + 1.$$

Adding these two equations gives

$$
\begin{aligned}
2S = \quad & 1 \; + \; 2 \; + \; \cdots \; + 99 + 100 \\
& + 100 + 99 + \; \cdots \; + \; 2 \; + \; 1.
\end{aligned}
$$

You can rearrange the expression on the right as a sum of 100 pairs of numbers, giving

$$2S = (1 + 100) + (2 + 99) + \cdots + (99 + 2) + (100 + 1).$$

Each of the 100 pairs in brackets has sum 101. Thus

$$2S = 100 \times 101, \quad \text{so} \quad S = \frac{100 \times 101}{2} = 5050.$$

This reverse order method can be used to find the formula for the sum of the first n natural numbers.

Activity 2 Finding a formula

Use the reverse order method to show that

$$1 + 2 + \cdots + n = \tfrac{1}{2}n(n+1).$$

(Hint: Begin by letting S denote the sum of the first n natural numbers.)

Any list of numbers is called a **sequence**. For example, $1, 2, 3, \ldots, 100$ is an example of a **finite sequence**, whereas $1, 2, 3, \ldots$ is an example of an **infinite sequence**. The numbers in a sequence are called the **terms** of the sequence.

An **arithmetic sequence** is a sequence with the property that the **difference** between consecutive terms is constant. For example,

$1, 2, 3, \ldots$ is an arithmetic sequence with difference 1,

$10, 8, \ldots, 4, 2, 0$ is an arithmetic sequence with difference -2,

$2, 2.5, 3, 3.5, 4$ is an arithmetic sequence with difference 0.5.

> An arithmetic sequence is sometimes called an **arithmetic progression**, and the difference is often called the **common difference**.

To specify an arithmetic sequence, we can give

* the first term, denoted by a

* the difference, denoted by d.

If the sequence is finite, we also give the number of terms, denoted by n. The first term a and the difference d can be any number, positive, negative or zero, but the number of terms n is always a positive integer.

For example, looking at each step of the final example given above,

$$\overset{+0.5}{2 \;\; \overset{+0.5}{2.5} \;\; \overset{+0.5}{3} \;\; \overset{+0.5}{3.5} \;\; 4},$$

you can see that this sequence can be specified with $a = 2$, $d = 0.5$ and $n = 5$.

Activity 3 Writing down arithmetic sequences

(a) Write down the arithmetic sequence with first term 3, difference 7, and 5 terms.

(b) Write down the arithmetic sequence with first term 3, difference -5, and 8 terms.

Let's look at the way that the successive terms of an arithmetic sequence develop. Suppose that the first term is a, the difference is d, and you want to find the nth term. Since the first term is a, the second term is

$$a + d,$$

and the third term is

$$a + d + d = a + 2d,$$

and so on. So the first few terms are

$$a, \; a + d, \; a + 2d, \; a + 3d, \; \ldots.$$

From the first term to the nth term there are exactly $n-1$ additions of d. This gives a formula for the nth term.

The nth term can be thought of as the last term of a finite sequence with n terms.

> The nth term of an arithmetic sequence with first term a and difference d is given by the formula
>
> $$n\text{th term} = a + (n-1)d.$$ (1)

For example, for the arithmetic sequence

$$2,\ 2.5,\ 3,\ 3.5,\ \ldots,$$

$a = 2$ and $d = 0.5$. So, by equation (1), the 9th term of this sequence is given by

$$2 + (9 - 1) \times 0.5 = 2 + 8 \times 0.5 = 6,$$

and the 100th term is given by

$$2 + (100 - 1) \times 0.5 = 2 + 99 \times 0.5 = 51.5.$$

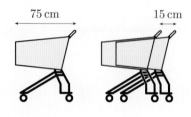

75 cm   15 cm

Figure 4 Calculating the length of stacked supermarket trolleys

Activity 4   Finding the nth term of an arithmetic sequence

Certain supermarket trolleys are 75 cm long and when stacked each trolley extends 15 cm beyond the one in front, as illustrated in Figure 4.

(a) Write down the lengths (in centimetres) of: one trolley, two stacked trolleys, and three stacked trolleys.

(b) The lengths in part (a) form the first three terms of an arithmetic sequence. Write down its first term a and its difference d.

(c) How long is a line of 20 stacked trolleys? Give your answer in metres.

Suppose that you are given an arithmetic sequence such as

$$3, 7, 11, \ldots, 35.$$

How can you find the number of terms, n, without writing them all out? If you denote the last term by L, then equation (1) for the nth term can be written as

$$L = a + (n - 1)d.$$

Rearranging formulas of this type was covered in Unit 7.

You can find a formula for the number of terms n by rearranging this formula to make n the subject.

Activity 5   Finding a formula for the number of terms

Rearrange the formula $L = a + (n-1)d$ to make n the subject. Assume that d is non-zero.

The solution to Activity 5 gives the following formula.

The number of terms n of a finite arithmetic sequence with first term a, last term L and non-zero difference d is given by the formula

$$n = \frac{L - a}{d} + 1. \tag{2}$$

Example 1 *Finding the number of terms*

For the arithmetic sequence

$$3, 7, 11, \ldots, 35,$$

write down the first term a, the difference d and the last term L, and find the number of terms n of the sequence.

Solution

For this sequence, the first term is $a = 3$, the difference is $d = 4$, and the last term is $L = 35$. So, by equation (2), the number of terms is

$$n = \frac{35 - 3}{4} + 1 = 8 + 1 = 9.$$

(Check: The sequence is $3, 7, 11, 15, 19, 23, 27, 31, 35$, which has 9 terms.)

Arithmetic sequences arise in various practical situations. For example, in some jobs the annual salary starts at a particular amount a and increases each year by a fixed amount d up to a certain maximum. Thus if you want to know the *total* amount earned in those years, then you need to find the sum of an arithmetic sequence with first term a and difference d.

This discussion ignores any changes due to annual inflation.

A formula for the sum of any finite arithmetic sequence can be found by using the reverse order method again. The sum of the arithmetic sequence with first term a, difference d and number of terms n is

$$S = a + (a + d) + (a + 2d) + \cdots + (a + (n - 1)d).$$

By adding this sum to the same sum in reverse order, you obtain

$$2S = a + (a + d) + (a + 2d) + \cdots + (a + (n - 1)d)$$
$$+ (a + (n - 1)d) + \cdots + (a + 2d) + (a + d) + a.$$

You can rearrange the expression on the right as a sum of pairs of numbers, each of which has sum $a + a + (n - 1)d$. There are n such pairs, so

$$2S = n(a + a + (n - 1)d) \quad \text{and hence} \quad S = \tfrac{1}{2}n(2a + (n - 1)d).$$

The sum of the finite arithmetic sequence with first term a, difference d and number of terms n is given by the formula

$$S = \tfrac{1}{2}n(2a + (n - 1)d).$$

An alternative version of this formula involving the last term L is

$$S = \tfrac{1}{2}n(a + L).$$

That is, S is n times the mean of the first and last terms.

This formula is often written as

$$S = \frac{n(2a + (n - 1)d)}{2}.$$

You can choose whichever version of this formula is more convenient!

Activity 6   Summing an arithmetic sequence

(a) For the arithmetic sequence

$$2, 5, 8, \ldots, 29,$$

write down the first term a, the difference d and the last term L, and hence find the number of terms n of the sequence.

(b) Find the sum of the arithmetic sequence in part (a).

The next activity asks you to use the formula for the sum of an arithmetic sequence in order to compare the total amount of pay offered by two jobs.

Activity 7   Finding the larger sum

Two jobs are advertised. In one, the annual salary starts at £20 000 and increases by £500 annually. In the other, the annual salary starts at £18 000 and increases by £1000 annually. Which job pays the greater total amount in the first 10 years?

You should assume that there are no changes due to inflation.

In this section, you've seen formulas for the sums of the first n natural numbers and the first n odd numbers. What about the sum of the first n even numbers:

$$2, 4, \ldots, 2n\,?$$

The numbers $2, 4, \ldots, 2n$ form an arithmetic sequence with first term $a = 2$ and last term $L = 2n$. So you can apply the formula to find the sum S of this sequence, as follows:

$$S = \tfrac{1}{2}n(a + L)$$
$$= \tfrac{1}{2}n(2 + 2n)$$
$$= n(n + 1).$$

An alternative way to find the sum of the first n even numbers is to spot that this sum is twice the sum of the first n natural numbers (found in Activity 2), so

$$2 + 4 + \cdots + 2n = 2(1 + 2 + \cdots + n)$$
$$= 2\left(\tfrac{1}{2}n(n + 1)\right) = n(n + 1).$$

The expression $n(n + 1)$ is the number of dots in a rectangle of n rows of $n + 1$ dots, as illustrated in Figure 2 on page 73. These numbers are called **oblong numbers** and are twice the triangular numbers, as you can see from Figure 2.

The various types of numbers that you have met have a history going back for thousands of years. Some of them played a role in the theories of the Pythagoreans about the significance of numbers.

The Pythagoreans (about 500 BC) were perhaps the first people to believe that numbers are important in their own right and not just for practical purposes. They named several different types of natural numbers, and linked some of them with properties and superstitions. For example:

- 1 was the source of all numbers

- the odd numbers $1, 3, 5, \ldots$ were masculine and divine

- the even numbers $2, 4, 6, \ldots$ were feminine and earthly

- the prime numbers $2, 3, 5, \ldots$ were one-dimensional (like a line) since a prime number of pebbles cannot be laid out to form a rectangle

- the triangular numbers $1, 3, 6, \ldots$ were considered to be very significant (perhaps because triangles are so important), especially the triangle of 10 dots, called the *tetractys* (Figure 5) which symbolised the four classical elements – earth, air, fire and water.

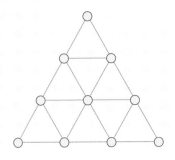

Figure 5   The tetractys

The triangular number 666 has a long history of notoriety. For example, in one translation of the Bible it is referred to as 'the number of the beast'. It is also the sum of the numbers on a roulette wheel, and it appears in various unusual mathematical identities.

These descriptions of numbers seem strange to modern eyes, but the obsession of the Pythagoreans and their later followers with the relationship between numbers and other aspects of life led to many discoveries, such as the role of numbers in determining musical scales.

In more recent times such sequences of numbers, especially prime numbers and triangular numbers, have been the objects of detailed study and found to have many intriguing mathematical properties. Gauss himself was particularly pleased to prove (at the age of 19) that every natural number can be expressed as the sum of at most three triangular numbers.

For example,
$$100 = 1 + 21 + 78.$$

1.2   Another number pattern

Here is another number pattern involving square numbers.

The following table shows values obtained by taking the numbers $1, 2, 3, \ldots$, squaring them, and then subtracting 1.

n	1	2	3	4	5	6	7
n^2	1	4	9	16	25	36	49
$n^2 - 1$	0	3	8	15	24	35	48

Now look at the numbers in the bottom row and consider writing each of them as a product of two factors that are as close together as possible. For example,

$$8 = 2 \times 4, \quad 15 = 3 \times 5 \quad \text{and} \quad 35 = 5 \times 7.$$

In all these examples, the two factors differ by 2 and lie immediately above and below the number that was squared:

$$3^2 - 1 = 8 = 2 \times 4 = (3 - 1)(3 + 1),$$
$$4^2 - 1 = 15 = 3 \times 5 = (4 - 1)(4 + 1),$$
$$6^2 - 1 = 35 = 5 \times 7 = (6 - 1)(6 + 1).$$

You can check that this pattern holds for the other values of n in this table; for example,

$$7^2 - 1 = 48 = 6 \times 8 = (7 - 1)(7 + 1).$$

On the basis of these examples, it is plausible to think that if n is any natural number, then

$$n^2 - 1 = (n-1)(n+1).$$

Recall from Unit 5 that an *identity* is an equation that is true for all values of the variables.

You can check quite quickly that this equation is true for all natural numbers less than 10, say, but does it hold for *all* natural numbers? In other words, is this equation an identity? In the next activity, you are asked to prove that $n^2 - 1 = (n-1)(n+1)$ by a geometric method, similar to one used for some of the other identities that you have met.

Activity 8   *Proving a number pattern*

(a) Look at the 5×5 square below, consisting of 25 regularly-spaced dots. By removing the dot in the top right corner and then moving the remaining 4 dots in the top row, construct a rectangle consisting of 24 dots.

   Explain how this construction is related to the equation $5^2 - 1 = 4 \times 6$.

(b) The construction in part (a) showed that the equation

$$n^2 - 1 = (n-1)(n+1)$$

   is true for $n = 5$. Explain how a similar construction can be used to show that this equation is true for all natural numbers n.

The diagram in the solution to Activity 8 enables you to 'see' why the identity $(n-1)(n+1) = n^2 - 1$ is true. Once you understand why a particular mathematical fact is true, it often happens that you can use similar reasoning to deduce other mathematical facts. For example, you can use similar geometric reasoning with an $n \times n$ square of dots to show that

Try drawing a 5×5 square of dots, removing a 2×2 square of dots from the top right corner, and rearranging the dots to make a rectangle.

$$n^2 - 4 = (n-2)(n+2).$$

However, identities like this one and the one in Activity 8 can also be proved *algebraically* by using the key algebraic skill of 'multiplying out pairs of brackets', as you will see in the next section.

2 Multiplying out pairs of brackets

2.1 Pairs of brackets

In Unit 5 you learned how to multiply out, or expand, brackets in expressions such as

$$2x(-3y + 2z).$$

There, you used the following strategy.

> **Strategy** *To multiply out brackets*
>
> Multiply each term inside the brackets by the multiplier of the brackets.

In the above expression, the multiplier is $2x$.

As a reminder, here are some examples of multiplying out brackets:

$$a(b + c) = ab + ac,$$
$$-2(x - y) = -2x + 2y,$$
$$3m(-2n + 3r - 6) = -6mn + 9mr - 18m.$$

You should also remember that if the multiplier *follows* the brackets, then you can apply the same strategy. The next activity gives you a chance to revise multiplying out brackets.

For example,
  $(b + c)a = ba + ca.$

> **Activity 9** *Multiplying out brackets*
>
> Multiply out the brackets in each of the following expressions.
>
> (a) $a(2b + 3c)$ (b) $-r(2s - 3t)$ (c) $(n - 1)n$

The key thing to remember is that you must multiply *each* term in the brackets by the multiplier.

In Section 1 you met an identity that involves a product of two brackets:

$$(n - 1)(n + 1) = n^2 - 1.$$

This identity was proved in Activity 8 by using a geometric argument. But it can also be proved by using algebra to multiply out the brackets in $(n - 1)(n + 1)$. Such products of brackets occur in many situations in mathematics, so it is important to be able to multiply them out correctly.

You can multiply out two brackets of the form

$$(a + b)(c + d)$$

in two steps, as follows.

- First, keep $(a + b)$ as one expression and use it as the multiplier to expand the right bracket $(c + d)$, to obtain

$$(a + b)(c + d) = (a + b)c + (a + b)d.$$

- Second, expand each of the $(a + b)$ brackets on the right-hand side:

$$(a + b)(c + d) = (a + b)c + (a + b)d$$
$$= ac + bc + ad + bd.$$

Alternatively, you could first expand the left bracket $(a + b)$, using $(c + d)$ as the multiplier. You can check that the answer is the same!

If you examine the effect of multiplying out the brackets in $(a + b)(c + d)$, then you can see that each term in the second bracket is multiplied by each term in the first bracket. This always happens when you multiply out two brackets, and it gives the following strategy.

> **Strategy** *To multiply out two brackets*
>
> Multiply each term inside the first bracket by each term inside the second bracket, and add the resulting terms.

When you use this strategy to multiply out

$$(a + b)(c + d),$$

you have to multiply each of the terms a and b in the first bracket by each of the terms c and d in the second bracket. It is a good idea to be systematic about the order in which you do these four multiplications. Figure 6 shows the order that is usually used in this module.

The acronym FOIL may help you to remember the order in which these pairs are multiplied. It stands for:

(1) First: ac,

(2) Outer: ad,

(3) Inner: bc,

(4) Last: bd.

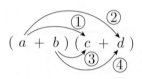

Figure 6 Order of multiplications

Here is the result:

$$(a + b)(c + d) = ac + ad + bc + bd.$$

Note that the answer obtained before the strategy above was a different arrangement of these four terms.

Of course, it is not essential to follow the order given in the above diagram. If you already have some experience of multiplying out pairs of brackets and have developed your own method of doing it, then that's fine as long as you obtain the correct answer!

If a, b, c and d represent positive numbers, then the rule for multiplying out brackets can be thought of in terms of areas of rectangles as follows. In Figure 7 the sides of the large rectangle are $a + b$ units and $c + d$ units, and this rectangle can be split into four smaller rectangles with areas ac, ad, bc and bd square units. Adding these four areas shows that the above expansion of the brackets is correct in this context.

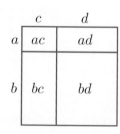

Figure 7 $(a + b)(c + d) = ac + ad + bc + bd$

As usual, you have to be careful when multiplying out brackets if minus signs are present. For example, you can use the strategy above to multiply out the product

$$(2s - t)(u - 3v),$$

but you must remember that the terms in the first bracket are $2s$ and $-t$, and the terms in the second bracket are u and $-3v$. It may help to mark these terms, as you did in Section 3 of Unit 5, before multiplying each term in the first bracket by each term in the second bracket:

$$(2s \; - t)(u \; - 3v) = 2su - 6sv - tu + 3tv.$$

$2s \times u = 2su,$
$2s \times (-3v) = -6sv,$
$(-t) \times u = -tu,$
$(-t) \times (-3v) = 3tv.$

The resulting four terms on the right-hand side have each been simplified in one step, as you learned to do in Unit 5.

Here are some more examples of multiplying out brackets.

Tutorial clip

Example 2   *Multiplying out two brackets*

Multiply out the brackets in each of the following expressions.

(a) $(x + 1)(x + 2)$ (b) $(x - 1)(x - 2)$ (c) $(x + 1)^2$

(d) $(a + 2b)(3c - d)$ (e) $(n - 1)(n + 1)$

Solution

(a) $(x + 1)(x + 2) = x^2 + 2x + x + 2 = x^2 + 3x + 2$

(b) $(x - 1)(x - 2) = x^2 - 2x - x + 2 = x^2 - 3x + 2$

(c) $(x + 1)^2 = (x + 1)(x + 1) = x^2 + x + x + 1 = x^2 + 2x + 1$

(d) $(a + 2b)(3c - d) = 3ac - ad + 6bc - 2bd$

(e) $(n - 1)(n + 1) = n^2 + n - n - 1 = n^2 - 1$

Part (e) of Example 2 is the number pattern identity mentioned in Subsection 1.2, so we have now succeeded in proving this identity algebraically!

The next activity gives you lots of practice in multiplying out brackets.

Activity 10   *Multiplying out two brackets*

Multiply out the brackets in each of the following expressions, simplifying the answer where appropriate.

(a) $(x + 2)(x + 4)$ (b) $(a + 2b)(3x + 4y)$ (c) $(x - 3)^2$

(d) $(a - 2b)(3c - d)$ (e) $(p - 1)(-2 + 3q)$ (f) $(n - 2)(n + 2)$

The strategy on page 82 can also be used to multiply out two brackets that contain more than two terms. Here a little more care is needed to ensure that all possible pairs of terms are included. For example, in the product

$$(a + b)(c + d + e),$$

each of the two terms in the first bracket must multiply each of the three terms in the second bracket, so there are $2 \times 3 = 6$ product terms in the answer. We obtain these terms in order, beginning with the products involving a and then the products involving b:

$$(a + b)(c + d + e) = a(c + d + e) + b(c + d + e)$$
$$= ac + ad + ae + bc + bd + be.$$

Activity 11   *Multiplying out longer brackets*

Multiply out the brackets in the expression $(2a - b)(c - 3d + 2e)$.

2.2 Squaring brackets

You have now multiplied out many pairs of brackets, including ones involving squaring, such as

$$(x + 1)^2 = (x + 1)(x + 1) = x^2 + x + x + 1 = x^2 + 2x + 1.$$

You often need to square brackets in this way, so it is a good idea to become familiar with this operation. Once again, there is a useful pattern to spot, which you can see in these examples:

$$(x + 1)^2 = x^2 + 2x + 1,$$
$$(x + 2)^2 = x^2 + 4x + 4,$$
$$(x + 3)^2 = x^2 + 6x + 9,$$
$$(x + 4)^2 = x^2 + 8x + 16.$$

In each case, in the expansion on the right,

- the coefficient of x is *twice* the number in the bracket on the left
- the constant term is the *square* of the number in the bracket on the left.

In general,

$$(x + p)^2 = (x + p)(x + p)$$
$$= x^2 + xp + px + p^2$$
$$= x^2 + 2px + p^2.$$

In other words, to square a bracket with two terms, you add together the square of the first term, the square of the last term, and twice the product of the two terms.

A similar pattern occurs when there is a negative sign in the brackets; for example:

$$(x - 1)^2 = x^2 - 2x + 1,$$
$$(x - 2)^2 = x^2 - 4x + 4,$$
$$(x - 3)^2 = x^2 - 6x + 9,$$
$$(x - 4)^2 = x^2 - 8x + 16.$$

Here the only difference is that a minus sign appears on each side.

> ### Squaring brackets
> $$(x + p)^2 = x^2 + 2px + p^2$$
> and
> $$(x - p)^2 = x^2 - 2px + p^2.$$

So, if you are asked to square brackets, then you may be able to write down the answer directly using one of these general identities (if the expression in brackets is $x + p$ or $x - p$, or of this form). Alternatively, you can multiply out the brackets in the usual way. Here are some questions for you to try.

Activity 12 *Squaring brackets*

Multiply out the following brackets.

(a) $(x + 7)^2$ (b) $(u - 10)^2$ (c) $(t + \frac{1}{2})^2$

(d) $(3x + 2)^2$ (e) $(2s - 5t)^2$

Squaring brackets can also be used to find tricks for squaring numbers in your head. These tricks can even form the basis of a career!

> Dr Arthur T. Benjamin is an American professor of mathematics and a professional magician. In a performance called 'Mathemagic', he does rapid mental calculations including squaring 2-, 3- and 4-digit numbers faster than his audience can square them with a calculator. He then explains how he uses simple algebraic techniques to do these mental feats.

To illustrate how algebra can explain such tricks, imagine that you want to square a two-digit number ending in 5. Such a number is of the form $10m + 5$, where m is a natural number; for example, $65 = 10 \times 6 + 5$, so $m = 6$ in this case, and $45 = 10 \times 4 + 5$, so $m = 4$ in this case.

Figure 8 Dr Arthur T. Benjamin

Here is a quick way to calculate the square of a number of this form.

> To square $10m + 5$, where m is a natural number:
>
> • calculate $m(m + 1)$
>
> • the required square is $100m(m + 1) + 25$.

For example, to find 65^2, where $m = 6$:

• $6 \times 7 = 42$

• $4200 + 25 = 4225$.

In the second step you can obtain the answer quickly by putting the digits 25 immediately after the number you found in the first step.

The secret of the trick is just that the square of $10m + 5$ is

$$(10m + 5)^2 = 100m^2 + 100m + 25.$$

Now $100m^2 + 100m$ can be factorised as $100m(m + 1)$, so the right-hand side can be rearranged to give

$$(10m + 5)^2 = 100m(m + 1) + 25.$$

The key idea here is to replace one apparently complicated calculation by several much easier ones. The difficulty is spotting what those easier calculations are. However, by using algebra you can manipulate one expression into another relatively easily and so not only find a simpler way of doing the calculation but also show that the new calculation works for all numbers of this form. This illustrates some of the power of using algebra and you'll see another example of this in the next section.

Multiplying a natural number by 100 is the same as writing two zeros at the end of it.

There are similar tricks based on algebra for squaring other two-digit numbers. You can find out more about these on the module website.

2.3   Differences of two squares

In Example 2 and Activity 10 on page 83 you were asked to multiply out pairs of brackets in which one bracket contains a sum of two numbers and the other bracket contains a difference of the same two numbers, such as

Here, the sum is $n + 1$ and the difference is $n - 1$.

$$(n - 1)(n + 1) = n^2 - 1.$$

This is another type of product that occurs so often in mathematics that it is worth learning the pattern in the answer. Here is the general case:

$$(x - p)(x + p) = x^2 + xp - px - p^2 = x^2 - p^2.$$

Because the form of the right-hand side in this identity is a difference of two squares, namely x^2 minus p^2, the identity is given this name.

> **Difference of two squares**
>
> $$(x - p)(x + p) = x^2 - p^2$$

So, if you are asked to find the product of two brackets of the form above, one a sum and the other the corresponding difference, then you may be able to write down the answer directly using this identity. For example,

Here you replace x by $2n$ and p by 1.

$$(2n - 1)(2n + 1) = (2n)^2 - 1^2 = 4n^2 - 1.$$

Alternatively, you can just multiply out the brackets in the usual way.

Here are some similar questions for you to try.

Activity 13   *Using a difference of two squares*

Use the difference of two squares identity to multiply out the following brackets.

(a) $(u - 12)(u + 12)$ (b) $(x - 2y)(x + 2y)$ (c) $(10 - a)(10 + a)$

Finally, the following story shows that the difference of two squares identity may help you to win a quiz!

A television quiz once asked a contestant to calculate $51^2 - 49^2$. At first sight, this appears to be quite a tricky calculation:

$$51^2 - 49^2 = 2601 - 2401 = 200.$$

However, by using a difference of two squares, the answer can be found in your head:

$$51^2 - 49^2 = (51 - 49)(51 + 49) = 2 \times 100 = 200.$$

3 Quadratic expressions and equations

Earlier in the module you learned how to *solve* various types of equations, that is, how to find the values of the unknowns in them. For example, you saw in Unit 5 how to solve equations such as

$$3(x + 1) = 12,$$

which is a single linear equation in the unknown x, and in Unit 7 how to solve

$$3x + 2y = 11,$$
$$2x - 3y = 3,$$

which is a pair of simultaneous linear equations in the unknowns x and y.

In this section you will meet a new type of equation, called a *quadratic equation*, and learn one way that such an equation can often be solved.

3.1 Quadratic expressions

If you expand the brackets in the product $(x + 1)(3x - 4)$, then you obtain

$$(x + 1)(3x - 4) = 3x^2 - 4x + 3x - 4$$
$$= 3x^2 - x - 4.$$

The resulting expression involves three terms:

- a term in x^2, namely $3x^2$
- a term in x, namely $-x$
- a constant term, namely -4.

An expression of the form

$$ax^2 + bx + c, \quad \text{where } a, b, c \text{ are numbers, and } a \neq 0,$$

is called a **quadratic expression** in x, or a quadratic in x, or just a **quadratic**.

The numbers a, b and c are called the **coefficients** of the quadratic.

Remember that the statement $a \neq 0$ is read as 'a is not equal to 0' or as 'a is non-zero'.

The Latin word 'quadrare' means 'to square'.

The coefficients b and c in a quadratic expression $ax^2 + bx + c$ can equal 0, but a must be non-zero, so that the expression includes a term in x^2. Also, you can write the terms of a quadratic in any order, but in this module we usually put them in the order above, with the term in x^2 first.

As usual, the variable in a quadratic expression can be any letter. For example:

- $x^2 + 2x - 3$ is a quadratic in x, with $a = 1$, $b = 2$ and $c = -3$
- $3t^2 + 1$ is a quadratic in t, with $a = 3$, $b = 0$ and $c = 1$
- $2x + 1$ is not a quadratic, as there is no term in x^2
- $3y^3 + y^2 + 1$ is not a quadratic, because it includes a power of y higher than a square.

Activity 14   *Identifying quadratic expressions*

Which of the following expressions are quadratics? For those that are quadratics, state the values of a, b and c.

(a) $9x^2 - 12x + 4$ (b) $3y - 5$ (c) $-6 - 7s^2$ (d) $2x^3 + x^2$

3.2   Quadratic equations

Any equation that can be expressed in the form

$$ax^2 + bx + c = 0$$

(by rearranging if necessary) is called a **quadratic equation** in x. In this equation, x is an unknown, and a, b and c are numbers with $a \neq 0$. One of the key techniques of algebra that you will learn in this module is how to solve a quadratic equation, that is, how to find the values of x that satisfy the equation.

Activity 15   *Checking a solution*

Show that $x = 2$ is a solution of the quadratic equation

$$2x^2 - x - 6 = 0.$$

There are many problems in mathematics that require you to solve a quadratic equation. You have already met some examples in Section 3 of Unit 8, where you used Pythagoras' Theorem to find side lengths in right-angled triangles. You will meet several more examples in this unit and the next.

The importance of quadratic equations has sometimes been called into question. For example, there was a debate in Parliament in 2003 about quadratic equations and whether they were 'irrelevant'. The closing speech of the debate included the following stirring words in support of the teaching of quadratic equations, and of mathematics in general!

'Quadratic equations allow us to analyse the relationships between variable quantities, and they are the tool for understanding variable rates of change. It is in variable rates of change that quadratic equations are seen in economics, science and engineering. Examples of the use of quadratic equations include acceleration, ballistics and financial comparisons ...

In conclusion, the teaching of quadratic equations, and of the mathematics curriculum overall, is key to a future work force that can develop and use mathematical models in daily life. As research in a book of quotations reveals, Napoleon said: "The advancement and perfection of mathematics are intimately connected with the prosperity of the state."'

Alan Johnson, Minister for Lifelong Learning, Further and Higher Education, 26 June 2003.

So how do quadratic equations occur? In Units 5 and 7 you saw that equations arise from problems in which you have to find an unknown number, by using the following strategy.

Strategy *To find an unknown number*

- Represent the number that you want to find by a letter.
- Express the information that you know about the number as an equation.
- Solve the equation.

Here is a problem (not a practical problem, however) in which finding an unknown number leads to a quadratic equation.

> Find a number with the property that if you square the number and add 6, then the answer is 5 times the number.

If you try some simple numbers, then you soon find that one answer is 2, because

$$2^2 + 6 = 10 \quad \text{and} \quad 5 \times 2 = 10.$$

But if you continue to search, then you find another solution, namely 3, because

$$3^2 + 6 = 15 \quad \text{and} \quad 5 \times 3 = 15.$$

The fact that there is more than one solution to this problem may seem strange at first – could there be further solutions?

To investigate, we can follow the strategy above. First, let x represent a number that has the given property. Then $x^2 + 6$ must be the same as $5x$; that is,

$$x^2 + 6 = 5x.$$

This equation can be rearranged to give the quadratic equation

$$x^2 - 5x + 6 = 0.$$

Thus if you know how to solve a quadratic equation, then you can solve the problem. In this case you can find two solutions without using the quadratic equation, as you saw, but if the numbers had been different, then using the quadratic equation might have been essential.

The above problem is just a puzzle, but it is intriguing because there are two possible solutions. In fact, it illustrates a type of problem used by Babylonian teachers almost 4000 years ago as part of the mathematical training of their scribes! For example, one of their problems was:

> If the sum of the area of a square and its side length is $\frac{3}{4}$, then what is the side length of the square?

When using mathematics to solve a *practical* problem, you should not add an area to a length, as the units are different.

The ancient Babylonians developed many skills such as agriculture, irrigation, writing and arithmetic. Their systems of trade required reliable methods of calculating areas and volumes, to find the volumes of grain in storage containers, for example. So they invented many techniques for solving numerical problems, including ones leading to quadratic equations. The problems that they used for teaching were often puzzles. Other problems involved measurements of fields and construction projects, usually in somewhat unrealistic settings.

You will see more examples of how quadratic equations arise later in this section, after you have met a method of solving them.

3.3 Solving simple quadratic equations

Some quadratic equations can be solved quite easily. For example, the simple equation

$$x^2 = 0$$

has the solution $x = 0$, and this is the only solution of this equation. The equation

$$x^2 - 4 = 0, \quad \text{or equivalently} \quad x^2 = 4,$$

can also be solved easily. It has the solution $x = 2$, since $2^2 = 4$, and it also has the solution $x = -2$, since $(-2)^2 = 4$.

You can write both of these solutions together as $x = \pm 2$.

The equation

$$x^2 = 2$$

Square roots were discussed in Unit 3.

can be solved in a similar way. It has the solution $x = \sqrt{2}$, since $(\sqrt{2})^2 = 2$, and it also has the solution $x = -\sqrt{2}$, since $(-\sqrt{2})^2 = 2$.

More generally, every equation of the form

$$x^2 = d, \quad \text{where } d > 0,$$

has two solutions, namely $x = \pm\sqrt{d}$.

 Tutorial clip

Example 3   *Solving simple quadratic equations*

Solve each of the following quadratic equations.

(a) $x^2 - 9 = 0$ (b) $t^2 - 10 = 0$

Solution

(a) This equation can be rearranged as $x^2 = 9$, so it has two solutions, $x = \pm 3$.

(b) This equation can be rearranged as $t^2 = 10$, so it has two solutions, $t = \pm\sqrt{10}$.

Here are two quadratic equations of this type for you to solve.

Activity 16   *Solving simple quadratics*

Solve each of the following quadratic equations.

(a) $x^2 - 25 = 0$ (b) $t^2 - 3 = 0$

Simple quadratic equations of this form are sometimes used by the police when investigating road traffic accidents. By measuring the length of a vehicle's skid mark, the speed of the vehicle at the start of the skid can be estimated by using the formula $s^2 = c\,d$, where d is the length of the skid mark in metres, s is the speed at the start of the skid in km/h, and c is a constant that depends on factors like the road surface and the condition of the vehicle. So the speed s is equal to $\sqrt{cd}$.

In contrast to these simple quadratic equations, there are others that seem to be impossible to solve. For example, the equation

$$x^2 + 1 = 0, \quad \text{or equivalently} \quad x^2 = -1,$$

has no solutions, at least among the real numbers, because when you square any real number the answer is not negative.

So, even among the simple quadratic equations in this subsection, there are equations that have one solution, two solutions or no solutions! These three different possibilities occur also for more complicated quadratic equations. You will see in Unit 10 why a quadratic equation never has more than two solutions. All the quadratic equations that you are asked to solve in this module have at least one solution.

In higher-level mathematics modules, so-called *complex numbers* are introduced in order to provide solutions to equations like $x^2 + 1 = 0$.

3.4 Factorising quadratics of the form $x^2 + bx + c$

In this subsection you will learn a technique that can often be used to solve a quadratic equation. The technique is to **factorise** the quadratic expression that appears in the equation; that is, to express the quadratic expression as a product of simpler expressions. Initially, we consider only quadratic expressions of the form $x^2 + bx + c$ (so the coefficient of x^2 is 1), where b and c are *integers*.

You saw earlier that multiplying out brackets like $(x + 2)(x + 3)$ leads to a quadratic expression:

$$\begin{aligned}(x + 2)(x + 3) &= x^2 + 3x + 2x + 6 \\ &= x^2 + 5x + 6.\end{aligned}$$

This shows that $x^2 + 5x + 6$ can be written as a product of the simpler expressions $x + 2$ and $x + 3$, each of which is called a **factor** of $x^2 + 5x + 6$.

But now suppose that you want to do the reverse process; that is, you want to *find* a factorisation of $x^2 + 5x + 6$:

$$x^2 + 5x + 6 = (\quad)(\quad),$$

where each of the two expressions in brackets on the right-hand side contains a term in x and a constant term. Because the term in x^2 in the quadratic expression is just x^2, the factorisation must be of the form

$$x^2 + 5x + 6 = (x \underline{\quad})(x \underline{\quad}),$$

where there is a positive or negative constant term in each of the gaps indicated. You can find these missing numbers by comparing the coefficients of the terms on both sides of the equation. When you multiply out the brackets on the right-hand side:

- the constant term that you get is the product of the two missing numbers, so this product is equal to the constant term on the left-hand side, which is 6

- the coefficient of the term in x that you get is the sum of the two missing numbers, so this sum is equal to the coefficient of x on the left-hand side, which is 5.

You can see these two facts happening in practice if you look at the working for $(x + 2)(x + 3)$ above, or try some similar examples yourself.

It is not hard to guess a pair of numbers whose product is 6 and whose sum is 5, namely $2, 3$, so this gives the required factorisation:

$$x^2 + 5x + 6 = (x + 2)(x + 3),$$

as expected.

See Unit 3 for a discussion of factor pairs.

A more systematic approach is to consider all factor pairs of 6 and choose the pair whose sum is 5. The only factorisations of 6 as a product of two positive numbers are

$$1 \times 6 \quad \text{and} \quad 2 \times 3.$$

Among these factor pairs, only the pair $2, 3$ has sum 5.

This approach is the basis of the following strategy for trying to factorise any quadratic expression of the form $x^2 + bx + c$, where b and c are integers.

> **Strategy** *To factorise* $x^2 + bx + c$*, where* b *and* c *are integers*
>
> Fill in the gaps in the brackets on the right-hand side of the equation
>
> $$x^2 + bx + c = (x \underline{\quad})(x \underline{\quad})$$
>
> with two numbers whose product is c and whose sum is b:
>
> $$x^2 + bx + c.$$
> $$\uparrow \qquad \uparrow$$
> $$\text{sum} \quad \text{product}$$
>
> You can search systematically for integers with these properties as follows:
>
> - write down the factor pairs of c, the constant term
> - choose (if possible) a pair whose sum is b, the coefficient of x.

If there is no pair of integers with these two properties, then a factorisation of the quadratic of the form $x^2 + bx + c = (x \underline{\quad})(x \underline{\quad})$, with integers in the gaps, is not possible. In this unit we concentrate on those quadratics that *can* be factorised using integers, but you should be aware that this is not possible for all quadratics.

Here is an example of this strategy in action.

Tutorial clip

Example 4 *Factorising a quadratic expression*

Factorise the quadratic expression $x^2 + 6x + 8$.

Solution

Find a pair of numbers whose product is 8 and whose sum is 6.

The positive factor pairs of 8 are

$$1, 8, \quad 2, 4.$$

The only pair whose sum is 6 is $2, 4$.

If you spot that the pair $2, 4$ has product 8 and sum 6 straight away, then there is no need to write down any other factor pairs.

Thus

$$x^2 + 6x + 8 = (x + 2)(x + 4).$$

(Check: Multiplying out the brackets gives

$$(x + 2)(x + 4) = x^2 + 4x + 2x + 8$$
$$= x^2 + 6x + 8.)$$

When using the strategy on the opposite page, you will often need to consider factor pairs of the constant term c that include negative factors; for example, $-1, -8$ and $-2, -4$ are factor pairs of 8. However, in Example 4 you needed to consider only positive factor pairs, because:

- the product of the factors, 8, is positive, so the factors must have the same sign as each other
- the sum of the factors, 6, is positive, so *both factors must be positive.*

So you needed to consider only the factor pairs $1, 8$ and $2, 4$.

The quadratics for you to factorise in Activity 17 are of this type.

The strategy on the opposite page suggests that you write down the possible factor pairs systematically. However, if you can spot the required factor pair, then there is no need to write down the others.

Activity 17 *Factorising quadratic expressions*

Factorise each of the following quadratic expressions.

(a) $x^2 + 3x + 2$ (b) $x^2 + 11x + 24$

Don't forget to check that your factorisations work!

In the solution to Activity 17(b), all positive factor pairs of 24 were listed for completeness. But when you solve such a problem, you could omit the pair $1, 24$, for example, since its sum is clearly not 11. Your aim is to find a factor pair that does work!

In the next example, the constant term c is again positive but b, the coefficient of x, is negative. In this case, you need to consider only negative factor pairs, because:

- the product of the factors is positive, so the factors must have the same sign as each other
- the sum of the factors is negative, so *both factors must be negative.*

Example 5 *Factorising a quadratic expression*

 Tutorial clip

Factorise the quadratic expression $x^2 - 5x + 6$.

Solution

💭 Find a pair of numbers whose product is 6 and whose sum is -5. 💭

The negative factor pairs of 6 are

$$-1, -6, \quad -2, -3.$$

The only pair whose sum is -5 is $-2, -3$.

Thus

$$x^2 - 5x + 6 = (x - 2)(x - 3).$$

(Check: Multiplying out the brackets gives

$$(x - 2)(x - 3) = x^2 - 3x - 2x + 6$$
$$= x^2 - 5x + 6.)$$

Here are some quadratics of this type for you to factorise.

Activity 18   *Factorising quadratic expressions*

Factorise each of the following quadratic expressions.

(a) $x^2 - 10x + 24$ (b) $t^2 - 4t + 3$ (c) $x^2 - 6x + 9$

In the next example, the constant term c is negative, so the numbers in the factor pairs of c must have opposite signs. This leads to more factor pairs than if c is positive.

Tutorial clip

Example 6   *Factorising a quadratic expression*

Factorise the quadratic expression $x^2 - 7x - 8$.

Solution

Find a pair of numbers whose product is -8 and whose sum is -7.

The factor pairs of -8 are

$$1, -8, \quad 2, -4, \quad -1, 8, \quad -2, 4.$$

The only pair whose sum is -7 is $1, -8$.

Thus

$$x^2 - 7x - 8 = (x + 1)(x - 8).$$

(Check: Multiplying out the brackets gives

$$(x + 1)(x - 8) = x^2 - 8x + x - 8$$
$$= x^2 - 7x - 8.)$$

Here are some quadratics of this type for you to factorise.

Activity 19   *Factorising quadratic expressions*

Factorise each of the following quadratic expressions.

(a) $x^2 - x - 2$ (b) $u^2 + 4u - 12$

Factorising special quadratic expressions

Some special quadratic expressions can be factorised more easily. For example, if there is no constant term (that is, if $c = 0$), then x is always a common factor. For example:

$$x^2 + 4x = x(x + 4),$$
$$x^2 - 6x = x(x - 6).$$

Another special factorisation occurs when the quadratic expression is a difference of two squares. For example:

$$x^2 - 1 = (x - 1)(x + 1), \quad \text{because} \quad x^2 - 1 = x^2 - 1^2,$$
$$x^2 - 9 = (x - 3)(x + 3), \quad \text{because} \quad x^2 - 9 = x^2 - 3^2.$$

Finally, you can sometimes recognise that a quadratic expression is a
perfect square; that is, it is equal to the square of a simpler expression,
because it is of the form

$$x^2 + 2px + p^2 \quad \text{or} \quad x^2 - 2px + p^2.$$

In these cases

$$x^2 + 2px + p^2 = (x + p)^2 \quad \text{or} \quad x^2 - 2px + p^2 = (x - p)^2,$$

as you saw in Subsection 2.2. For example, the quadratic expression
$x^2 - 6x + 9$ from Activity 18 is of the form

$$x^2 - 2px + p^2, \quad \text{with } p = 3.$$

This shows, without using the strategy, that

$$x^2 - 6x + 9 = (x - 3)^2.$$

Activity 20 *Factorising special quadratic expressions*

Factorise each of the following quadratic expressions.

(a) $x^2 - x$ (b) $u^2 - 16$ (c) $t^2 - 9t$ (d) $x^2 + 10x + 25$

3.5 Solving quadratic equations by factorisation

Suppose now that you want to solve the quadratic equation

$$x^2 - 5x + 6 = 0. \tag{3}$$

In Example 5 you saw that you can factorise the quadratic expression

$$x^2 - 5x + 6 \quad \text{as} \quad (x - 2)(x - 3).$$

So you can rewrite equation (3) as

$$(x - 2)(x - 3) = 0.$$

How does this rewriting of the equation help? Well, this new equation
states that the product of the two numbers $x - 2$ and $x - 3$ is 0. So you
can use the following property of numbers.

> If the product of two or more numbers is 0, then at least one of the
> numbers must be 0.

This property is true because if
two numbers are both non-zero,
then their product is non-zero.

You can apply this property to the above factorisation to deduce that

$$x - 2 = 0 \quad \text{or} \quad x - 3 = 0.$$

If $x - 2 = 0$, then $x = 2$, and if $x - 3 = 0$, then $x = 3$. So the quadratic
equation (3) has two solutions:

$$x = 2 \quad \text{and} \quad x = 3.$$

Here is a check that these values of x do indeed satisfy equation (3):

$$\text{when } x = 2, \quad x^2 - 5x + 6 = 2^2 - 5 \times 2 + 6 = 4 - 10 + 6 = 0,$$
$$\text{when } x = 3, \quad x^2 - 5x + 6 = 3^2 - 5 \times 3 + 6 = 9 - 15 + 6 = 0.$$

In general, you can use the following strategy.

> **Strategy**   To solve $x^2 + bx + c = 0$ by factorisation
>
> 1. Find a factorisation:
> $$x^2 + bx + c = (x + p)(x + q).$$
> 2. Then $(x + p)(x + q) = 0$, so
> $$x + p = 0 \quad \text{or} \quad x + q = 0,$$
> and hence the solutions are
> $$x = -p \quad \text{and} \quad x = -q.$$

The numbers p and q may be positive, negative or zero.

Note that the two solutions of a quadratic equation may be the same; in this case the equation is said to have a **repeated solution**.

Once you have found the solutions, it is a good idea to check that they both satisfy the equation $x^2 + bx + c = 0$.

Here is an example of this strategy in action.

 Tutorial clip

Example 7   *Solving a quadratic equation*

Solve $x^2 - 7x - 8 = 0$ by factorisation.

Solution

The equation is: $x^2 - 7x - 8 = 0$

This factorisation was found in Example 6.

Factorise: $(x + 1)(x - 8) = 0$

So: $x + 1 = 0 \quad \text{or} \quad x - 8 = 0$

So: $x = -1 \quad \text{or} \quad x = 8$

(Check: When $x = -1$,
$$x^2 - 7x - 8 = (-1)^2 - 7 \times (-1) - 8 = 1 + 7 - 8 = 0.$$
When $x = 8$,
$$x^2 - 7x - 8 = 8^2 - 7 \times 8 - 8 = 64 - 56 - 8 = 0.)$$

Here are some quadratic equations for you to solve.

Activity 21   *Solving equations by factorisation*

Solve each of the following quadratic equations by factorisation.

You factorised several of these quadratics in earlier activities.

(a) $x^2 + 3x + 2 = 0$ (b) $x^2 - 10x + 24 = 0$ (c) $t^2 - 16 = 0$

(d) $u^2 - u - 12 = 0$ (e) $x^2 - 6x + 9 = 0$ (f) $x^2 - 9x = 0$

Factorisation is an efficient method of solving quadratic equations when it can be applied. However, as stated earlier, not all quadratics of the form $x^2 + bx + c$ can be factorised in the form $(x + p)(x + q)$ using integers p and q. In Unit 10 you will meet a formula for solving a quadratic equation which avoids the need for factorisation.

3.6 Factorising quadratics of the form $ax^2 + bx + c$

You have now seen how to factorise quadratic expressions of the form $x^2 + bx + c$, whenever this is possible using integers. It's also possible to factorise many expressions in which the coefficient of x^2 is not 1, as you will now see.

Sometimes, factorising a quadratic expression of the form $ax^2 + bx + c$, where a is not 1, can be reduced to the case when the first term is x^2 because a is a common factor of the coefficients. For example, in the quadratic $2x^2 + 10x + 12$, each of the coefficients is a multiple of 2, so

$$2x^2 + 10x + 12 = 2(x^2 + 5x + 6).$$

You saw earlier that $x^2 + 5x + 6 = (x + 2)(x + 3)$, so

$$2x^2 + 10x + 12 = 2(x + 2)(x + 3).$$

Activity 22   *Factorising when the coefficients have a common factor*

Factorise each of the following quadratic expressions.

(a) $3x^2 - 3x - 36$ (b) $-5x^2 + 15x - 10$

However, consider the quadratic expression

$$2x^2 - x - 6.$$

The presence of the coefficient 2 in the term $2x^2$ means that a factorisation of the form $(x + p)(x + q)$ is not possible; also, 2 is not a common factor of the coefficients. A factorisation using integers *may* still be possible though, and below are two methods that you can use to try to find one. You can use either method, but if you have already met one of them and are confident in using it, then you may prefer to continue to use your method.

Remember that many quadratics do not factorise using integers.

The first method is based on checking all possibilities.

Example 8   *Factorising a general quadratic expression – first method*

 Tutorial clip

Factorise $2x^2 - x - 6$.

Solution

First note that the terms in x in the brackets must be $2x$ and x. Then try to find a factorisation of the form

$$2x^2 - x - 6 = (2x \underline{\quad})(x \underline{\quad}),$$

where the gaps each contain a positive or negative integer.

The two missing integers must have product -6.

The possible factor pairs of -6 are

$$-1, 6, \quad 1, -6, \quad -2, 3, \quad 2, -3.$$

These four factor pairs lead to eight possible cases:

$$(2x - 1)(x + 6) \quad \text{or} \quad (2x + 6)(x - 1),$$
$$(2x + 1)(x - 6) \quad \text{or} \quad (2x - 6)(x + 1),$$
$$(2x - 2)(x + 3) \quad \text{or} \quad (2x + 3)(x - 2),$$
$$(2x + 2)(x - 3) \quad \text{or} \quad (2x - 3)(x + 2).$$

By multiplying out each of these pairs of brackets in turn, you find that one of these cases is the required factorisation, specifically,

$$(2x + 3)(x - 2) = 2x^2 - 4x + 3x - 6$$
$$= 2x^2 - x - 6.$$

Thus

$$2x^2 - x - 6 = (2x + 3)(x - 2).$$

You can often use this first method efficiently by deciding which are the most likely cases (for example, by considering which signs are possible) and checking these cases first. But the method can be time consuming because there may be many cases to consider. For example, if the first term of the quadratic is $6x^2$, then you have to consider brackets starting with $6x$ and x, and also with $3x$ and $2x$.

In the second method, you need to consider fewer cases but it is not immediately clear why the method works. Indeed, explaining why it works requires a higher level of mathematics than is appropriate in this module. At this stage you should concentrate on learning the technique, which is described in the green text.

Tutorial clip

Example 9 *Factorising a general quadratic expression – second method*

Factorise $2x^2 - x - 6$.

Solution

The quadratic expression is of the form $ax^2 + bx + c$, where $a = 2$, $b = -1$ and $c = -6$.

💭 First, find two numbers whose product is ac and whose sum is b. 💭

For this quadratic expression, $ac = 2 \times (-6) = -12$ and $b = -1$.

The possible factor pairs of -12 are

$$-1, 12, \quad 1, -12, \quad -2, 6, \quad 2, -6, \quad -3, 4, \quad 3, -4.$$

The only pair whose sum is -1 is $3, -4$.

💭 Next, rewrite the quadratic expression, splitting the term in x using the above factor pair. 💭

Since $-1 = 3 - 4$,

$$2x^2 - x - 6 = 2x^2 + 3x - 4x - 6.$$

💭 Finally, group the four terms in pairs and take out common factors to give the required factorisation. 💭

Then

$$2x^2 - x - 6 = \underline{2x^2 + 3x} \; \underline{- 4x - 6}$$
$$= x(2x + 3) - 2(2x + 3)$$
$$= (x - 2)(2x + 3).$$

💭 Here, the first pair of terms on the RHS has a common factor of x and the second pair has a common factor of -2, and then both expressions $x(2x + 3)$ and $-2(2x + 3)$ have a common factor of $(2x + 3)$. 💭

Thus

$$2x^2 - x - 6 = (x - 2)(2x + 3).$$

Note that the second method works in whichever order you split the middle term:

$$2x^2 - x - 6 = 2x^2 - 4x + 3x - 6$$
$$= 2x(x - 2) + 3(x - 2)$$
$$= (2x + 3)(x - 2).$$

In the following activity you can use either the first method or the second method.

Activity 23   *Factorising a general quadratic expression*

Factorise each of the following quadratic expressions.

(a) $2x^2 - 5x + 3$ (b) $6x^2 + 7x - 3$ (c) $8x^2 - 10x - 3$

Once you have factorised a quadratic expression, you can solve the corresponding quadratic equation. In Examples 8 and 9 you saw that

$$2x^2 - x - 6 = (2x + 3)(x - 2).$$

Therefore the equation

$$2x^2 - x - 6 = 0$$

can be written as

$$(2x + 3)(x - 2) = 0.$$

Hence the solutions of this equation satisfy

$$2x + 3 = 0 \quad \text{or} \quad x - 2 = 0.$$

If $2x + 3 = 0$, then $2x = -3$ so $x = -\frac{3}{2}$.

If $x - 2 = 0$, then $x = 2$.

Hence the solutions are

$$x = -\frac{3}{2} \quad \text{and} \quad x = 2.$$

Here are some general quadratic equations for you to solve.

Activity 24   *Solving general quadratic equations*

Use your answers to Activity 23 to solve each of the following quadratic equations.

(a) $2x^2 - 5x + 3 = 0$ (b) $6x^2 + 7x - 3 = 0$ (c) $8x^2 - 10x - 3 = 0$

Before you start to solve a quadratic equation it is a good idea to check that it is in its simplest form as this can make it easier to work with. Here are some things that you can do to simplify a quadratic equation.

> **Simplifying a quadratic equation**
> - If the coefficient of x^2 is negative, then multiply the equation through by -1 to make this coefficient positive.
> - If the coefficients have a common factor, then divide the equation through by this factor.
> - If any of the coefficients are fractions, then multiply the equation through by a suitable number to clear them.

For example, to solve the equation

$$-5x^2 + 15x - 10 = 0,$$

you can multiply through by -1 to obtain

$$5x^2 - 15x + 10 = 0.$$

Then divide the equation through by the common factor 5 to obtain

$$x^2 - 3x + 2 = 0,$$

which factorises to give

$$(x - 1)(x - 2) = 0.$$

So the solutions of this equation are $x = 1$ and $x = 2$.

If the sum of the area of a square and its side length is $\frac{3}{4}$, then what is the side length of the square?

Finally, the ancient Babylonian problem mentioned on page 89 leads to the equation

$$x^2 + x = \tfrac{3}{4}, \quad \text{which can be rearranged as} \quad x^2 + x - \tfrac{3}{4} = 0.$$

You can obtain an equivalent quadratic equation with coefficients that are integers by clearing fractions in the usual way. Multiplying through by 4 gives the equation

$$4x^2 + 4x - 3 = 0.$$

This quadratic expression can be factorised using either the first or second method to give

$$4x^2 + 4x - 3 = (2x - 1)(2x + 3).$$

The solutions satisfy $2x - 1 = 0$ or $2x + 3 = 0$, so they are $x = \frac{1}{2}$ and $x = -\frac{3}{2}$. However, the problem was to find the side length of a square, so x is positive. Thus the answer to this problem is $x = \frac{1}{2}$.

3.7 Problems leading to quadratic equations

Quadratic equations arise in many problems, as you will now see.

Example 10   *Using a quadratic equation*

Two walkers start from the same point. The first walks east at 4 mph. The second starts half an hour after the first and walks north, also at 4 mph. How long after the first walker sets out are they 10 miles apart?

Solution

Let t denote the time in hours after which the walkers are 10 miles apart.

Remember that distance = speed × time.

After t hours the first walker has covered $4t$ miles. The second walker starts half an hour later, so after t hours has walked for $t - \frac{1}{2}$ hours, and so has covered $4(t - \frac{1}{2}) = 4t - 2$ miles.

This diagram shows the situation when the two walkers are 10 miles apart.

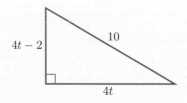

By Pythagoras' Theorem,

$$(4t)^2 + (4t-2)^2 = 10^2. \tag{4}$$

Pythagoras' Theorem was discussed in Unit 8, Section 3.

Now $(4t)^2 = 16t^2$ and $(4t-2)^2 = 16t^2 - 16t + 4$, so equation (4) can be written as

$$16t^2 + 16t^2 - 16t + 4 = 100.$$

This equation can be rearranged as

$$32t^2 - 16t - 96 = 0; \quad \text{that is,} \quad 2t^2 - t - 6 = 0,$$

Here, both sides are divided by 16.

which is a quadratic equation.

The factorisation of $2t^2 - t - 6$ was found in Example 8:

$$2t^2 - t - 6 = (2t+3)(t-2).$$

In Example 8 the variable was x rather than t.

This factorisation shows that the solutions of this equation satisfy

$$2t + 3 = 0 \quad \text{or} \quad t - 2 = 0.$$

Hence $t = -\frac{3}{2}$ or $t = 2$.

Since a negative number makes no sense as a solution here, the answer to the question is 2 hours.

(Check: After 2 hours the first walker has gone 8 miles and the second has gone 6 miles, so, by Pythagoras' Theorem, their distance apart is indeed $\sqrt{8^2 + 6^2} = 10$ miles.)

In Example 10, a negative number was rejected as a possible answer. In general, when answering mathematical questions by solving equations you should use the following principle.

> If a mathematical question leads to an equation with more than one solution, then you should accept as possible answers only those solutions that make sense for the original question.

Here are some more questions that can be answered by finding a suitable quadratic equation and solving it using factorisation.

Activity 25 *Finding an unknown side length*

The diagram shows a right-angled triangle. The side lengths are measured in centimetres.

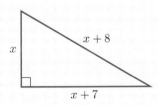

(a) Apply Pythagoras' Theorem to obtain an equation involving x.

(b) Rearrange the equation to obtain a quadratic equation for x, and hence find the value of x.

Activity 26   *Finding the width of a garden*

The diagram shows a rectangular garden that is twice as long as it is wide. Around the edge is a path 1 m wide that surrounds a rectangular lawn with area $40\,\text{m}^2$.

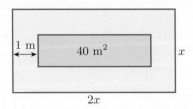

How wide is the garden?

To end this section, here are some details of the life of one of the first people to use quadratic equations, and many other types of equations, to solve real-world problems.

Figure 9   Thomas Harriot (1560–1621)

In this way, Harriot anticipated the much later development of complex numbers.

Thomas Harriot was an English astronomer and mathematician. He worked for Sir Walter Raleigh (also spelt Ralegh), providing mathematical information on practical matters such as navigation and the optimal method of stacking cannonballs, and later for Henry Percy, Duke of Northumberland, who had a great interest in scientific questions. Unfortunately, Harriot published very little, but he is now credited with being the first person to view the Moon through a telescope and make a drawing of it, the first to view sunspots, and the first to state Snell's law of refraction in optics.

Harriot taught courses on navigation (based on 'spherical' trigonometry) to Raleigh's seamen, and in mathematics he established many of the basics of algebra needed to solve quadratic equations and equations involving higher powers of the unknown x, such as x^3, drawing on the work of the French mathematician Viète.

Harriot introduced a simplified notation for doing algebra (though he still wrote a^2 as aa, a^3 as aaa, and so on) and he understood the idea of factorisation of quadratics and expressions involving higher powers of the unknown x. He also used negative solutions of equations and even solutions that involved square roots of negative numbers.

4 Manipulating algebraic fractions

As you saw in Unit 5, fractions that involve algebraic expressions are called **algebraic fractions**. Here are some examples:

$$\frac{8ab}{c}, \quad \frac{1}{(x-3)^2} \quad \text{and} \quad \frac{2x+1}{x^2+1}.$$

Algebraic fractions appear in many important formulas. For example,

$$F = \frac{GmM}{r^2}$$

is a formula for the force of gravitational attraction F between two objects that have masses m and M, and are a distance r apart; here G is a constant, called the *universal gravitational constant*, measured in suitable units.

To be able to work with such formulas, you need to be able to manipulate algebraic fractions in a similar way to numerical fractions. For example, you should be able to add them and multiply them. In this section you will practise working with algebraic fractions, and in the next section you will meet some problems that are solved by manipulating algebraic fractions.

"I'd like to meet you halfway, but I'm terrible with fractions."

When you work with algebraic fractions, there is a risk of considering values of the variables for which the denominator of the fraction is 0. Since dividing by 0 is not allowed, you need to avoid using such values of the variables! For example, the formula above for the force F due to gravity cannot be applied with $r = 0$. In fact, r takes only positive values, since it represents a distance between two different objects.

4.1   Equivalent algebraic fractions

Recall from Section 3 of Unit 3 that two numerical fractions are **equivalent** if one can be obtained from the other by multiplying or dividing both the numerator and the denominator by the same number. For example,

$$\frac{2}{6} \quad \text{is equivalent to} \quad \frac{1}{3}, \quad \text{because} \quad \frac{2}{6} = \frac{1 \times 2}{3 \times 2}.$$

Similarly, two algebraic fractions are equivalent if one can be obtained from the other by multiplying or dividing both the numerator and the denominator by the same expression. For example,

$$\frac{a}{b} \quad \text{is equivalent to} \quad \frac{a(a+1)}{b(a+1)}.$$

However, notice that the first expression here is valid for $a = -1$, whereas the second expression is not.

The process of simplifying a numerical fraction by dividing both the numerator and the denominator by the same number is called **cancelling** a common factor. For example, the fraction $\frac{2}{6}$ can be simplified by cancelling the common factor 2:

$$\frac{2}{6} = \frac{\overset{1}{\cancel{2}}}{\underset{3}{\cancel{6}}} = \frac{1}{3}.$$

Algebraic fractions can be simplified in the same way, by cancelling any common factors of the numerator and denominator. You can represent the cancellation in the usual way, by crossing out the expressions with common factors and writing the results of the cancellations nearby.

This crossing out is not always shown, however.

You can find any common factors of the numerator and denominator of an algebraic fraction by expressing the numerator and denominator as products of all their factors, if this is not done already. Here are some examples.

Tutorial clip

Example 11   *Simplifying algebraic fractions*

Simplify each of the following algebraic fractions.

(a) $\dfrac{a^2}{a^5}$ (b) $\dfrac{60p^3q}{35p^5r}$ (c) $\dfrac{2x^2+6x}{x^2-9}$

Solution

(a) 🗨 Divide top and bottom by a^2. 🗨

$$\frac{a^2}{a^5} = \frac{\overset{1}{\cancel{a^2}}}{\underset{a^3}{\cancel{a^5}}} = \frac{1}{a^3}$$

🗨 Now top and bottom have no common factors, so the fraction can't be simplified further. 🗨

(b) 🗨 Divide top and bottom by 5 and p^3. 🗨

$$\frac{60p^3q}{35p^5r} = \frac{\overset{12}{\cancel{60}}\overset{1}{\cancel{p^3}}q}{\underset{7}{\cancel{35}}\underset{p^2}{\cancel{p^5}}r} = \frac{12q}{7p^2r}$$

(c) 🗨 To find any common factors, factorise the top and bottom. 🗨

The denominator x^2-9 is a difference of two squares.

$$\frac{2x^2+6x}{x^2-9} = \frac{2x(x+3)}{(x-3)(x+3)} = \frac{2x\overset{1}{\cancel{(x+3)}}}{(x-3)\underset{1}{\cancel{(x+3)}}} = \frac{2x}{x-3}$$

In Example 11, the expressions that are factors of the denominators are all assumed to be non-zero. For example, in part (a) it is assumed that $a \neq 0$. Similarly, in part (c) it is assumed that $x-3 \neq 0$ and $x+3 \neq 0$. Often, assumptions of this type are not stated explicitly, but you should be aware of them.

It is important to cancel only expressions that are *factors* of both the numerator and the denominator of a fraction. For example, in the fraction

$$\frac{2x^2+6x}{x^2-9},$$

in Example 11, it would have been wrong to cancel the expression x^2 in the numerator and denominator, because x^2 is not a factor of the numerator or denominator. So before you cancel anything, check that it is a factor of both the top and the bottom!

Here are some algebraic fractions for you to simplify.

Activity 27   *Simplifying algebraic fractions*

In part (d), you need to factorise both the numerator and the denominator.

Simplify the following algebraic fractions.

(a) $\dfrac{x^4}{x^9}$ (b) $\dfrac{20a^2b}{15ab^2}$ (c) $\dfrac{x^2+6x}{3x^2}$ (d) $\dfrac{u^2-4}{u^2+4u+4}$

4.2 Adding and subtracting algebraic fractions

The rules for adding and subtracting algebraic fractions are the same as those for adding and subtracting numerical fractions, which were given in Section 2 of Unit 3.

Here are some numerical examples. If the denominators are the same, then you just add or subtract the numerators:

$$\frac{3}{5} - \frac{2}{5} = \frac{1}{5}.$$

If the denominators are different, then you need to write the fractions with a common denominator before you can add or subtract them. For example, $\frac{2}{5}$ and $\frac{3}{8}$ can be added or subtracted by using the common denominator $5 \times 8 = 40$, as follows:

$$\frac{2}{5} + \frac{3}{8} = \frac{2 \times 8}{5 \times 8} + \frac{3 \times 5}{8 \times 5} = \frac{16}{40} + \frac{15}{40} = \frac{31}{40},$$

$$\frac{2}{5} - \frac{3}{8} = \frac{2 \times 8}{5 \times 8} - \frac{3 \times 5}{8 \times 5} = \frac{16}{40} - \frac{15}{40} = \frac{1}{40}.$$

The idea of finding a common denominator works for algebraic fractions too – the general strategy is given below.

> **Strategy** *To add or subtract algebraic fractions*
>
> 1. Make sure that the fractions have a common denominator – if necessary, rewrite each fraction as an equivalent fraction.
>
> 2. Add or subtract the numerators.
>
> 3. Simplify the answer by cancelling wherever possible.

Here are some examples to illustrate this strategy.

Example 12 *Adding and subtracting algebraic fractions*

Tutorial clip

Write each of the following expressions as a single algebraic fraction.

(a) $\dfrac{3}{x} - \dfrac{2}{x}$ (b) $\dfrac{3}{a+1} + \dfrac{2}{a+1} - \dfrac{1}{a+1}$ (c) $\dfrac{a}{x} + \dfrac{b}{y}$

Solution

(a) The denominators are the same, so subtract the numerators.

$$\frac{3}{x} - \frac{2}{x} = \frac{3-2}{x} = \frac{1}{x}$$

(b) The denominators are the same, so add and subtract the numerators.

$$\frac{3}{a+1} + \frac{2}{a+1} - \frac{1}{a+1} = \frac{3+2-1}{a+1} = \frac{4}{a+1}$$

(c) The product of the denominators is xy, so use this as a common denominator.

$$\frac{a}{x} + \frac{b}{y} = \frac{ay}{xy} + \frac{bx}{xy} = \frac{ay+bx}{xy}$$

As illustrated in Example 12(c), when you want to add or subtract algebraic fractions that do not have a common denominator, you can always obtain a common denominator by multiplying together the denominators of the given fractions.

Activity 28 *Adding and subtracting algebraic fractions*

Write each of the following expressions as a single algebraic fraction.

(a) $\dfrac{6}{y} + \dfrac{1}{y}$ (b) $\dfrac{x}{a^2} + \dfrac{y}{a^2} - \dfrac{z}{a^2}$ (c) $\dfrac{a}{2x} - \dfrac{b}{3y}$ (d) $\dfrac{1}{3x} - \dfrac{2}{x+3}$

Although you can always obtain a common denominator by multiplying together the denominators of the given fractions, there is sometimes a simpler common denominator. In the example

$$\frac{2}{a} + \frac{1}{a^2},$$

the product of the denominators is $a \times a^2 = a^3$. But a simpler common denominator is a^2, because a^2 is a multiple of both a and a^2. Using this common denominator gives

$$\frac{2}{a} + \frac{1}{a^2} = \frac{2a}{a^2} + \frac{1}{a^2} = \frac{2a+1}{a^2}.$$

If you had used the common denominator a^3, then the result would have been the same, but only after cancelling a common factor of a from the numerator and the denominator.

To find the simplest common denominator, you should factorise the denominators of the given fractions, if possible, and then choose the simplest expression that is a multiple of each denominator. For example, to write

$$\frac{x}{xy + y^2} + \frac{y}{x^2 + xy}$$

as a single algebraic fraction, you should factorise the denominators to give

$$\frac{x}{y(x+y)} + \frac{y}{x(x+y)}$$

and then choose as your common denominator $xy(x+y)$. So

$$\frac{x}{xy+y^2} + \frac{y}{x^2+xy} = \frac{x}{y(x+y)} + \frac{y}{x(x+y)}$$
$$= \frac{x^2}{xy(x+y)} + \frac{y^2}{xy(x+y)}$$
$$= \frac{x^2+y^2}{xy(x+y)}.$$

Also, when working with fractions you sometimes need to make an expression into a fraction in order to combine it with another fraction. For example, to express

$$a + \frac{2}{b}$$

as a single fraction, you can write a as the fraction $a/1$, and then choose the common denominator to be b:

$$a + \frac{2}{b} = \frac{a}{1} + \frac{2}{b} = \frac{ab}{b} + \frac{2}{b} = \frac{ab+2}{b}.$$

Activity 29 *Choosing denominators*

Write each of the following expressions as a single algebraic fraction.

(a) $\dfrac{5}{x^4} - \dfrac{4}{x^2}$
(b) $\dfrac{1}{x^2 + x} - \dfrac{1}{x + 1}$
(c) $a + \dfrac{a}{b + 3}$

4.3 Multiplying and dividing algebraic fractions

The rules for multiplying and dividing algebraic fractions are the same as those for multiplying and dividing numerical fractions, which were given in Section 2 of Unit 3.

Here are some numerical examples. To multiply two numerical fractions, multiply the numerators together and multiply the denominators together:

$$\frac{1}{5} \times \frac{3}{5} = \frac{1 \times 3}{5 \times 5} = \frac{3}{25}.$$

To divide by a numerical fraction, multiply by its reciprocal:

$$\frac{1}{5} \div \frac{3}{5} = \frac{1}{5} \times \frac{5}{3} = \frac{1 \times \overset{1}{\cancel{5}}}{\cancel{5} \times 3} = \frac{1}{3}.$$

Remember that to obtain the reciprocal of a fraction, you swap the numerator and denominator; in other words, you 'turn the fraction upside down'.

> **Strategy** *To multiply or divide algebraic fractions*
>
> - To multiply two algebraic fractions, multiply the numerators together and multiply the denominators together:
> $$\frac{a}{b} \times \frac{c}{d} = \frac{ac}{bd}.$$
> - To divide one algebraic fraction by another, multiply the first fraction by the reciprocal of the second fraction:
> $$\frac{a}{b} \div \frac{c}{d} = \frac{a}{b} \times \frac{d}{c} = \frac{ad}{bc}.$$
>
> In each case, you should cancel any common factors that appear.

The following examples illustrate this strategy.

Example 13 *Multiplying algebraic fractions*

 Tutorial clip

Write each of the following expressions as a single algebraic fraction, simplifying your answer if possible.

(a) $\dfrac{a}{2x} \times \dfrac{b}{3y}$
(b) $\dfrac{3x}{5y} \times \dfrac{y(y + 1)}{x^2}$

Solution

(a) $\dfrac{a}{2x} \times \dfrac{b}{3y} = \dfrac{a \times b}{2x \times 3y} = \dfrac{ab}{6xy}$

(b) $\dfrac{3x}{5y} \times \dfrac{y(y + 1)}{x^2} = \dfrac{3x \times y(y + 1)}{5y \times x^2} = \dfrac{3\overset{1}{\cancel{x}} \times \overset{1}{\cancel{y}}(y + 1)}{5\underset{1}{\cancel{y}} \times \underset{x}{\cancel{x^2}}} = \dfrac{3(y + 1)}{5x}$

Tutorial clip

Example 14   *Dividing algebraic fractions*

Write each of the following expressions as a single algebraic fraction, simplifying your answer if possible.

(a) $\dfrac{a}{2x} \div \dfrac{b}{3y}$ (b) $\dfrac{3x}{5y} \div \dfrac{y(y+1)}{x^2}$

Solution

(a) $\dfrac{a}{2x} \div \dfrac{b}{3y} = \dfrac{a}{2x} \times \dfrac{3y}{b} = \dfrac{a \times 3y}{2x \times b} = \dfrac{3ay}{2bx}$

(b) $\dfrac{3x}{5y} \div \dfrac{y(y+1)}{x^2} = \dfrac{3x}{5y} \times \dfrac{x^2}{y(y+1)} = \dfrac{3x \times x^2}{5y \times y(y+1)} = \dfrac{3x^3}{5y^2(y+1)}$

There are also some special cases of multiplying and dividing fractions. These arise when one of the expressions being multiplied or divided is not written as a fraction.

For example, you can do the following multiplication and division by writing $3b^2$ as a fraction with denominator 1:

$$3b^2 \times \dfrac{1}{a} = \dfrac{3b^2}{1} \times \dfrac{1}{a} = \dfrac{3b^2}{a}$$

and

$$\dfrac{b}{b+1} \div 3b^2 = \dfrac{b}{b+1} \div \dfrac{3b^2}{1} = \dfrac{b}{b+1} \times \dfrac{1}{3b^2} = \dfrac{1}{3b(b+1)}.$$

Here and from now on, the crossing out for any cancellation is not shown, but you may choose to include it if you find it helpful.

Here are some examples of multiplying and dividing algebraic fractions for you to try.

Activity 30   *Multiplying and dividing fractions*

Write each of the following expressions as a single algebraic fraction, simplifying your answer if possible.

(a) $\dfrac{p^2}{q^2} \times \dfrac{p}{q}$ (b) $\dfrac{p^2}{q^2} \div \dfrac{p}{q}$ (c) $\dfrac{9ax^2}{b} \times \dfrac{b^3}{4xy^2}$

(d) $\dfrac{9ax^2}{b} \div \dfrac{b^3}{4xy^2}$ (e) $8u^2 \times \dfrac{2}{u^2+u}$

To end this section, here is a practical application of dividing fractions.

Activity 31   *Finding the ratio of two forces*

In this activity, the mass of the Earth is M kg and its radius is R km, and the mass of the Moon is m kg and its radius is r km. The gravitational force acting on an object of mass 1 kg is given by the formulas

$$F = \frac{GM}{R^2} \quad \text{on the surface of the Earth}$$

and

$$f = \frac{Gm}{r^2} \quad \text{on the surface of the Moon,}$$

where G is a constant.

(a) Express the ratio F/f as an algebraic fraction involving M, m, R and r.

(b) Assuming that $M = 80m$ and $R = 4r$, deduce that $F = 5f$.

The actual values, to two significant figures, are as follows:
$$M = 6.0 \times 10^{24},$$
$$R = 6400,$$
$$m = 7.4 \times 10^{22},$$
$$r = 1700.$$

The data above show that these equations are approximately correct.

Part (b) of Activity 31 shows that the gravitational force acting on an object on the surface of the Earth is approximately five times greater than the gravitational force acting on the same object on the surface of the Moon. One dramatic consequence of this fact is that an astronaut can jump five times higher on the Moon than on the Earth! However, for a direct comparison the astronaut would have to wear the same spacesuit on Earth as on the Moon.

5 Rearranging formulas

Many branches of science are concerned with the relationship between different variables that are connected together in some way. For example, in physics the equation

$$PV = kT$$

relates the pressure P, volume V and temperature T of an enclosed quantity of a gas. Here k is a constant. In the form stated above, this equation does not have a subject (a single variable that appears only once, on its own on the left-hand side), but the formula can easily be rearranged to make P, for example, the subject:

$$P = \frac{kT}{V}.$$

The first version of this equation was published in 1662 by the Irish scientist Robert Boyle.

From this formula, you can see that if the temperature of the gas remains the same but the volume decreases, then the pressure of the gas increases.

The next subsection shows you how to solve equations by rearranging algebraic fractions. The final two subsections show you how to rearrange formulas that involve algebraic fractions or powers.

5.1 Solving equations by clearing algebraic fractions

In Section 5 of Unit 5 you saw a strategy for solving linear equations. This involved carrying out a sequence of steps of the following types:

- do the same thing to both sides
- simplify one side or both sides
- swap the sides.

You saw that the strategy can be applied to solve equations such as

$$3\left(1 + \frac{x}{2}\right) = 2(x - 1). \tag{5}$$

The first step is to multiply both sides of the equation by 2 to clear the fraction on the left. Then you multiply out the brackets and rearrange the terms so that the unknown x is left by itself on one side of the equation. The complete sequence of steps is as follows:

Multiply by 2: $\qquad 6\left(1 + \frac{x}{2}\right) = 4(x - 1)$

Multiply out the brackets: $\quad 6 + 3x = 4x - 4$

Subtract $3x$ and add 4: $\qquad 10 = x$

This gives the answer $x = 10$, and you can check that this value of x satisfies equation (5).

An equation involving algebraic fractions can be solved in a similar way. Usually the best first step is to clear the fractions, and this can be done by multiplying both sides of the equation by an expression that is a multiple of all the denominators, as illustrated in the next example.

Example 15 *Solving an equation by clearing algebraic fractions*

Solve the equation

$$\frac{2}{x} = \frac{1}{x - 1}.$$

Solution

If $x = 0$ or $x = 1$, then one of the fractions is undefined.

Assume that $x \neq 0$ and $x \neq 1$.

Multiply by $x(x - 1)$, which is a multiple of both x and $x - 1$.

Multiply by $x(x - 1)$: $\qquad x(x - 1)\dfrac{2}{x} = x(x - 1)\dfrac{1}{x - 1}$

Cancel: $\qquad 2(x - 1) = x$

Multiply out: $\qquad 2x - 2 = x$

Rearrange: $\qquad x = 2$

The value $x = 2$ satisfies the assumptions, so it is the solution.

(Check: When $x = 2$,

$$\text{LHS} = \frac{2}{2} = 1 \quad \text{and} \quad \text{RHS} = \frac{1}{2 - 1} = 1.)$$

In the next example, clearing the algebraic fractions gives a quadratic equation, which you can factorise using the methods of Section 3.

Example 16 *Solving another equation by clearing algebraic fractions*

Solve the equation
$$\frac{2}{x} + 3 = \frac{x+10}{4}.$$

Solution

Assume that $x \neq 0$.

🗨 Multiply by $4x$, which is a multiple of both x and 4. Use brackets to show that the *whole* of each side is multiplied by $4x$. 🗨

Multiply by $4x$:
$$4x\left(\frac{2}{x} + 3\right) = 4x\left(\frac{x+10}{4}\right)$$

Cancel on the RHS:
$$4x\left(\frac{2}{x} + 3\right) = x(x+10)$$

Multiply out both sides:
$$8 + 12x = x^2 + 10x$$

Subtract $8 + 12x$ and swap sides:
$$x^2 - 2x - 8 = 0$$

Factorise:
$$(x-4)(x+2) = 0$$

This gives $x = 4$ or $x = -2$, and these values satisfy the assumptions, so they are the solutions.

(Check: When $x = 4$,
$$\text{LHS} = \frac{2}{4} + 3 = 3\tfrac{1}{2} \quad \text{and} \quad \text{RHS} = \frac{4+10}{4} = 3\tfrac{1}{2}.$$

When $x = -2$,
$$\text{LHS} = \frac{2}{-2} + 3 = -1 + 3 = 2 \quad \text{and} \quad \text{RHS} = \frac{-2+10}{4} = \frac{8}{4} = 2.)$$

Here are some equations involving algebraic fractions for you to solve.

Activity 32 *Solving equations involving algebraic fractions*

Solve each of the following equations.

(a) $\dfrac{4}{x-3} = \dfrac{12}{x+1}$ (b) $\dfrac{t}{5} = \dfrac{2}{t+3}$

(c) $\dfrac{4}{x} + 2x = 9$ (d) $\dfrac{10}{x} + \dfrac{20}{x+40} = \dfrac{1}{2}$

There is a technique called *cross-multiplying* that can cut down a little of the work when you rearrange equations like those in parts (a) and (b) of this activity. You can learn about it in Unit 14.

In the two examples in this subsection, assumptions were made about the value of the unknown, to ensure that the denominators of the fractions were non-zero. These assumptions also ensured that the expressions by which both sides of the equations were multiplied were non-zero. In general, when you are trying to solve an equation, you should not multiply both sides by an expression that might be zero. To see why, consider the simple equation

$$x - 1 = 0. \tag{6}$$

This equation has just one solution, namely $x = 1$. Now look at what happens when you multiply both sides by the expression $x - 2$.

You obtain the equation

$$(x - 1)(x - 2) = 0,$$

which has *two* solutions, $x = 1$ and $x = 2$. So multiplying an equation by an expression can generate extra solutions that were not solutions of the original equation.

You can get round this problem by assuming that any expression that you multiply by is non-zero. Then, at the end of your working, you should check that the solutions that you have obtained satisfy the assumptions that you made, and disregard any solutions that do not. For example, you can multiply equation (6) by the expression $x - 2$ *provided that you assume that $x \neq 2$*. At the end of your working, you would disregard the solution $x = 2$, leaving you with just the correct solution $x = 1$.

Multiplying by $x - 2$ would not be a sensible way to solve equation (6), of course!

5.2 Rearranging formulas by clearing algebraic fractions

In Section 2 of Unit 7 you saw how to rearrange an equation to make a chosen variable the subject, by using the following strategy. This strategy is closely related to the techniques used in the previous subsection to solve equations.

Strategy   *To make a variable the subject of an equation*

Carry out a sequence of steps. In each step, do one of the following:

- do the same thing to both sides
- simplify one side or both sides
- swap the sides.

Aim to do the following, in order.

1. Clear any fractions and multiply out any brackets. To clear fractions, multiply both sides by a suitable expression.

2. Add or subtract terms on both sides to get all the terms containing the required subject on one side, and all the other terms on the other side.

3. If more than one term contains the required subject, then take it out as a common factor. This gives an equation of the form

$$\left(\text{an expression}\right) \times \left(\text{the required subject}\right) = \left(\text{an expression}\right).$$

4. Divide both sides by the expression that multiplies the required subject.

Here is an example of this strategy in action, from Section 2 of Unit 7.

Suppose that you are asked to make s the subject of the equation

$$r = \frac{s}{r} + 2s.$$

Multiply by r (assuming that $r \neq 0$): $r^2 = r\left(\dfrac{s}{r} + 2s\right)$

Multiply out: $r^2 = s + 2rs$

Take out s as a common factor: $r^2 = s(1 + 2r)$

Divide by $1 + 2r$ (assuming that $1 + 2r \neq 0$): $\dfrac{r^2}{1 + 2r} = s$

Swap the sides: $s = \dfrac{r^2}{1 + 2r}$

The first two steps in this list clear the fraction s/r in the original equation.

Let's look at an example that is a little more complicated than the examples that you saw in Unit 7: it involves more than one algebraic fraction.

In optics, the *lens formula*,

$$\frac{1}{f} = \frac{1}{u} + \frac{1}{v},$$

relates:

- the *focal length* f of a lens, that is, the distance from the lens at which (distant) parallel rays of light are focused

- the *object distance* u, that is, the distance from the lens of the object being viewed

- the *image distance* v, that is, the distance from the lens of the image of the object.

These distances are illustrated in Figure 10. The schematic diagram in part (a) of the figure shows a simple demonstration of how a lens can be used to project the image of a candle onto a screen. Five representative light rays are shown travelling from the candle, through the lens, to form the image on the screen. With this arrangement, the resulting image appears inverted.

Figure 10(b) shows the associated *ray diagram* for this scenario. Here you can see the object distance u, image distance v and focal length f, which are related by the lens formula.

> Strictly speaking, the lens formula is not a formula in the sense defined in Unit 2 (since it does not have a subject – a variable that appears only once, on its own on one side), but the word 'formula' is sometimes used loosely in mathematics.

> Ray diagrams are used in optics to describe how lenses can form images of varying size and shape, depending on the type of lens and how they are focused.

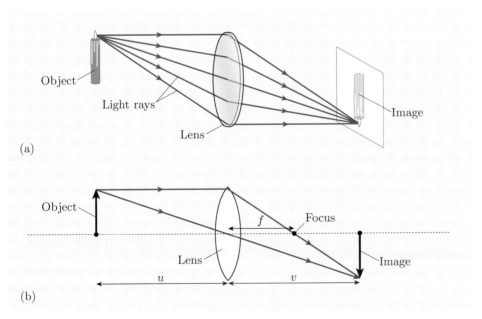

Figure 10 (a) Image formed by projecting an object through a convex lens. (b) Ray diagram of the scenario illustrated in (a).

The lens formula plays a fundamental role in optics; for example, it is used in the design of lenses for correcting eye disorders such as long-sightedness and short-sightedness.

The example below involves making a particular variable the subject of the lens formula.

Tutorial clip

Example 17   Rearranging the lens formula

Make u the subject of the lens formula

$$\frac{1}{f} = \frac{1}{u} + \frac{1}{v}.$$

Solution

To clear all the fractions, multiply both sides by f, u and v. Assume that $f \neq 0$, $u \neq 0$ and $v \neq 0$.

Multiply both sides by the product fuv:

$$\frac{fuv}{f} = \frac{fuv}{u} + \frac{fuv}{v}.$$

Cancel:

$$uv = vf + uf.$$

Get all the terms containing the required subject u on the left and all other terms on the right.

Rearrange the equation:

$$uv - uf = vf.$$

Take out u as a common factor:

$$u(v - f) = vf.$$

Now assume that $v - f \neq 0$. Then you can divide both sides by $v - f$ to give u as the subject:

$$u = \frac{vf}{v - f}.$$

You can make v or f the subject of the lens formula in a similar way:

$$v = \frac{uf}{u - f}, \quad \text{assuming that } u - f \neq 0,$$

and

$$f = \frac{uv}{u + v}, \quad \text{assuming that } u + v \neq 0.$$

Here are some rearrangements of this type for you to try.

Activity 33   Changing the subject

(a) Make u the subject of the equation $v = \dfrac{2}{u + 3} + 4$.

(b) Make x the subject of the equation $y = \dfrac{20}{3x} - \dfrac{3}{2}$.

As you saw in Unit 7, there is often more than one way to rearrange a formula to make a new variable the subject. For example in Activity 33(a), you could have begun by subtracting 4 from both sides:

$$v - 4 = \frac{2}{u + 3}.$$

Then if you multiply by $u + 3$ to clear the fraction, and divide by $v - 4$ (assuming that $u + 3 \neq 0$ and $v - 4 \neq 0$), you obtain

$$u + 3 = \frac{2}{v - 4}.$$

Subtracting 3 and then putting the right-hand side over a common denominator gives

$$u = \frac{2}{v - 4} - 3 = \frac{2}{v - 4} - \frac{3(v - 4)}{v - 4} = \frac{2 - 3(v - 4)}{v - 4} = \frac{14 - 3v}{v - 4}.$$

5.3   Formulas involving powers

In this last subsection, you will see how to change the subject of a formula involving powers. This involves using several properties of powers that were given in Unit 3.

For example, the formula

$$A = \pi r^2$$

expresses the area A of a circle in terms of its radius r and the constant $\pi = 3.141\,59\ldots$. This formula involves the power r^2.

"I don't know, it's a little formulaic."

Suppose that you want to rearrange this formula to make r the subject; that is, to get r by itself, just on the left-hand side of the equation. Once again you have to do this by carrying out a sequence of steps of the following types:

- do the same thing to both sides
- simplify one side or both sides
- swap the sides.

You can use steps of these types to get r^2 on its own on the left-hand side, as follows.

Divide by π: $\qquad \dfrac{A}{\pi} = r^2$

Swap the sides: $\qquad r^2 = \dfrac{A}{\pi}$

We can now get r on its own by taking the square root of both sides:

$$r = \pm\sqrt{\frac{A}{\pi}}.$$

We can apply the square root operation to the right-hand side because the expression A/π is positive (because A is an area).

Since r is a length, it is positive or zero, so the negative square root can be disregarded. Hence the formula is

$$r = \sqrt{\frac{A}{\pi}},$$

in which r is the subject.

See Unit 3 for a discussion of square roots and other roots.

The formula for r, obtained above, can be rewritten in various forms, such as

$$r = \left(\frac{A}{\pi}\right)^{\frac{1}{2}}, \quad r = \frac{A^{\frac{1}{2}}}{\pi^{\frac{1}{2}}} \quad \text{and} \quad r = \frac{\sqrt{A}}{\sqrt{\pi}}.$$

These forms are obtained by using the fact that taking the square root of a positive number is the same as raising the number to the power $\frac{1}{2}$, together with the rule $\sqrt{a/b} = \sqrt{a}/\sqrt{b}$.

In making r the subject of this formula, we used the same strategy as before, but here we applied a new operation to both sides of the equation, namely taking the square root of both sides, which is allowed only if both sides of the equation are positive.

Just as raising to the power $\frac{1}{2}$ is the reverse of squaring, so raising to the power $\frac{1}{3}$ is the reverse of raising to the power 3, and so on. We can extend the list of operations that we can apply to both sides of an equation, to include raising to a power, as long as we only apply this operation to *positive* quantities.

Thus if you can rearrange an equation into the form

$$\underbrace{\text{the required subject}}\ \overbrace{\text{a power}} = \underbrace{\text{an expression}},$$

where the expression on the right-hand side is positive, then you can obtain the required subject on its own on the left-hand side by raising both sides to the reciprocal of the power that the required subject is raised to.

Here is an example.

Tutorial clip

Example 18   Rearranging an equation with powers

The volume V of a sphere of radius r is given by the formula

$$V = \tfrac{4}{3}\pi r^3.$$

Make r the subject of this formula.

Solution

Multiply by 3:	$3V = 4\pi r^3$
Divide by 4π:	$\dfrac{3V}{4\pi} = r^3$
Swap the sides:	$r^3 = \dfrac{3V}{4\pi}$
Raise to the power $\frac{1}{3}$:	$r = \left(\dfrac{3V}{4\pi}\right)^{\frac{1}{3}}$

Here, the expression $\dfrac{3V}{4\pi}$ is positive because V is a volume.

Here are some similar rearrangements for you to try.

Activity 34   *Rearranging equations with powers*

(a) The volume V of a cone whose base has radius r and whose height is h (Figure 11) is given by the formula

$$V = \tfrac{1}{3}\pi r^2 h.$$

   (i)   Make r the subject of this formula.

   (ii) Hence find, to three significant figures, the base radius of a cone whose height is $1\,\mathrm{m}$ and whose volume is $2\,\mathrm{m}^3$.

(b) The *Tressider formula* was used in the nineteenth century for designing a ship's armour plating. It is

$$T^2 = \frac{MS^3}{cD},$$

where T is the required thickness of the armour plating, S is the speed of a shell fired at the ship, D is its diameter and M is its mass, and c is a constant.

Make S the subject of this formula.

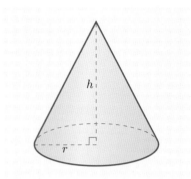

Figure 11   A cone

The key thing to remember when rearranging equations and formulas is always to do the same operation to both sides!

Learning checklist

After studying this unit, you should be able to:

- find the sum of any arithmetic sequence
- prove simple number patterns involving square numbers
- multiply out pairs of brackets
- solve quadratic equations by using factorisation, where possible
- add, subtract, multiply and divide algebraic fractions
- solve certain equations involving algebraic fractions
- rearrange certain formulas involving algebraic fractions and powers.

Solutions and comments on Activities

Activity 1

We can rearrange the numbers in the sum in pairs as follows:

$$1 + 2 + \cdots + 199 + 200$$
$$= (1 + 200) + (2 + 199) + \cdots + (100 + 101).$$

There are 100 pairs of numbers in brackets, and each pair has sum 201, so

$$1 + 2 + \cdots + 199 + 200 = 100 \times 201 = 20\,100.$$

Activity 2

Denote the sum of the first n natural numbers by S. Then

$$S = 1 + 2 + \cdots + (n-1) + n$$

and, in reverse order,

$$S = n + (n-1) + \cdots + 2 + 1.$$

By adding these two equations and rearranging the right-hand side, you obtain

$$2S = (1 + n) + (2 + (n-1)) + \cdots$$
$$+ ((n-1) + 2) + (n+1).$$

In this sum there are n pairs of numbers altogether, each pair having sum $n + 1$. Thus

$$2S = n \times (n+1), \quad \text{so} \quad S = \tfrac{1}{2}n(n+1).$$

Activity 3

(a) $3, 10, 17, 24, 31$

(b) $3, -2, -7, -12, -17, -22, -27, -32$

Activity 4

(a) One trolley has length 75 cm. Two stacked trolleys have length

$$75\,\text{cm} + 15\,\text{cm} = 90\,\text{cm}.$$

Three stacked trolleys have length

$$90\,\text{cm} + 15\,\text{cm} = 105\,\text{cm}.$$

(b) These lengths form the arithmetic sequence

$$75, 90, 105, \ldots.$$

So $a = 75$ and $d = 15$.

(c) The length of 20 stacked trolleys (in centimetres) is given by the 20th term in this sequence. By equation (1), the 20th term is

$$75 + (20 - 1) \times 15 = 75 + 285 = 360.$$

So the length of 20 stacked trolleys is 3.6 m.

Activity 5

The equation is: $L = a + (n-1)d$

Subtract a: $L - a = (n-1)d$

Swap sides: $(n-1)d = L - a$

Divide by d: $n - 1 = \dfrac{L - a}{d}$

Add 1: $n = \dfrac{L - a}{d} + 1$

Activity 6

(a) This arithmetic sequence has first term $a = 2$, difference $d = 3$ and last term $L = 29$. The number of terms n of the sequence is given by

$$n = \frac{29 - 2}{3} + 1 = 9 + 1 = 10.$$

(Check: The sequence is $2, 5, 8, 11, 14, 17, 20, 23,$ $26, 29$, which has 10 terms.)

(b) From part (a) the number of terms is 10, so we use the formula with $n = 10$:

$$S = \tfrac{1}{2}n(2a + (n-1)d)$$
$$= \tfrac{1}{2} \times 10(4 + 9 \times 3) = 155.$$

So the sum of the sequence is 155.

(Alternatively you can use the formula involving the last term:

$$S = \tfrac{1}{2}n(a + L) = \tfrac{1}{2} \times 10 \times (2 + 29) = 5 \times 31 = 155.)$$

Activity 7

The first salary scale is an arithmetic sequence with first term $a = 20\,000$, difference $d = 500$ and number of terms $n = 10$. Thus the total amount paid over 10 years, in pounds, is

$$S = \tfrac{1}{2}n(2a + (n-1)d)$$
$$= \tfrac{1}{2} \times 10 \times (2 \times 20\,000 + 9 \times 500)$$
$$= 5 \times (40\,000 + 4500) = 222\,500.$$

The second salary scale is an arithmetic sequence with first term $a = 18\,000$, difference $d = 1000$ and number of terms $n = 10$. Thus the total amount paid over 10 years, in pounds, is

$$S = \tfrac{1}{2}n(2a + (n-1)d)$$
$$= \tfrac{1}{2} \times 10 \times (2 \times 18\,000 + 9 \times 1000)$$
$$= 5 \times (36\,000 + 9000) = 225\,000.$$

Therefore the second job pays (slightly) more over 10 years.

Activity 8

(a) After the dot in the top right corner is removed, the four dots remaining in the top row can be moved to one of the sides to make a 4×6 rectangle of dots.

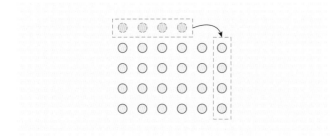

Before the four dots were moved there were $5^2 - 1$ dots, and afterwards there are 4×6 dots. This illustrates the equation $5^2 - 1 = 4 \times 6$.

(b) Consider a square consisting of n^2 dots. This can be converted into a rectangle consisting of $(n-1)(n+1)$ dots by removing the top right corner dot and moving a line of $n-1$ dots from the top row to the right side. Hence

$$n^2 - 1 = (n-1)(n+1).$$

Activity 9

(a) $a(2b + 3c) = 2ab + 3ac$

(b) $-r(2s - 3t) = -2rs + 3rt$

(c) $(n-1)n = n^2 - n$

Activity 10

(a) $(x+2)(x+4) = x^2 + 4x + 2x + 8$
$$= x^2 + 6x + 8$$

(b) $(a + 2b)(3x + 4y) = 3ax + 4ay + 6bx + 8by$

(c) $(x-3)^2 = (x-3)(x-3)$
$$= x^2 - 3x - 3x + 9$$
$$= x^2 - 6x + 9$$

(d) $(a - 2b)(3c - d) = 3ac - ad - 6bc + 2bd$

(e) $(p-1)(-2+3q) = -2p + 3pq + 2 - 3q$

(f) $(n-2)(n+2) = n^2 + 2n - 2n - 4 = n^2 - 4$

Activity 11

$(2a - b)(c - 3d + 2e)$
$= 2a(c - 3d + 2e) - b(c - 3d + 2e)$
$= 2ac - 6ad + 4ae - bc + 3bd - 2be$

Activity 12

(a) Writing down the answer directly gives
$(x + 7)^2 = x^2 + 14x + 49$.

(b) Writing down the answer directly gives
$(u - 10)^2 = u^2 - 20u + 100$.

(c) Writing down the answer directly gives
$(t + \tfrac{1}{2})^2 = t^2 + 2 \times \tfrac{1}{2}t + (\tfrac{1}{2})^2$
$$= t^2 + t + \tfrac{1}{4}.$$

(d) Multiplying out the brackets gives
$(3x + 2)^2 = (3x + 2)(3x + 2)$
$$= (3x)^2 + 6x + 6x + 2^2$$
$$= 9x^2 + 12x + 4.$$

(e) Multiplying out the brackets:
$(2s - 5t)^2 = (2s - 5t)(2s - 5t)$
$$= (2s)^2 - 10st - 10st + (5t)^2$$
$$= 4s^2 - 20st + 25t^2.$$

Activity 13

(a) By the difference of two squares identity,
$(u - 12)(u + 12) = u^2 - 12^2 = u^2 - 144$.

(b) By the difference of two squares identity,
$(x - 2y)(x + 2y) = x^2 - (2y)^2 = x^2 - 4y^2$.

(c) By the difference of two squares identity,
$(10 - a)(10 + a) = 10^2 - a^2 = 100 - a^2$.

Activity 14

(a) $9x^2 - 12x + 4$ is a quadratic, with $a = 9$, $b = -12$ and $c = 4$.

(b) $3y - 5$ is not a quadratic, as it has no squared term.

(c) $-6 - 7s^2$ is a quadratic, with $a = -7$, $b = 0$ and $c = -6$.

(d) $2x^3 + x^2$ is not a quadratic, as it has a term in x^3.

Activity 15

Substituting $x = 2$ in the quadratic expression gives
$$2x^2 - x - 6 = 2 \times 2^2 - 2 - 6$$
$$= 8 - 2 - 6 = 0.$$

Hence $x = 2$ is a solution of the equation.

Activity 16

(a) This equation can be rearranged as $x^2 = 25$, so it has two solutions, $x = \pm 5$.

(b) This equation can be rearranged as $t^2 = 3$, so it has two solutions, $t = \pm\sqrt{3}$.

Activity 17

(a) The quadratic is $x^2 + 3x + 2$.

The pair $1, 2$ has sum 3 and product 2. Thus
$$x^2 + 3x + 2 = (x + 1)(x + 2).$$
(Check: Multiplying out the brackets gives
$$(x + 1)(x + 2) = x^2 + 2x + x + 2$$
$$= x^2 + 3x + 2.)$$

(b) The quadratic is $x^2 + 11x + 24$.

The positive factor pairs of 24 are
$$1, 24, \quad 2, 12, \quad 3, 8, \quad 4, 6.$$
The only pair whose sum is 11 is $3, 8$. Thus
$$x^2 + 11x + 24 = (x + 3)(x + 8).$$
(Check: Multiplying out the brackets gives
$$(x + 3)(x + 8) = x^2 + 8x + 3x + 24$$
$$= x^2 + 11x + 24.)$$

Activity 18

(a) The quadratic is $x^2 - 10x + 24$.

The negative factor pairs of 24 are
$$-1, -24, \quad -2, -12, \quad -3, -8, \quad -4, -6.$$
The only pair whose sum is -10 is $-4, -6$. Thus
$$x^2 - 10x + 24 = (x - 4)(x - 6).$$
(Check: Multiplying out the brackets gives
$$(x - 4)(x - 6) = x^2 - 6x - 4x + 24$$
$$= x^2 - 10x + 24.)$$

(b) The quadratic is $t^2 - 4t + 3$.

The pair $-1, -3$ has product 3 and sum -4. Thus
$$t^2 - 4t + 3 = (t - 1)(t - 3).$$
(Check: Multiplying out the brackets gives
$$(t - 1)(t - 3) = t^2 - 3t - t + 3$$
$$= t^2 - 4t + 3.)$$

(c) The quadratic is $x^2 - 6x + 9$.

The negative factor pairs of 9 are
$$-1, -9, \quad -3, -3.$$
The only pair whose sum is -6 is $-3, -3$. Thus
$$x^2 - 6x + 9 = (x - 3)(x - 3) = (x - 3)^2.$$
(Check: Multiplying out the brackets gives
$$(x - 3)(x - 3) = x^2 - 3x - 3x + 9$$
$$= x^2 - 6x + 9.)$$

Activity 19

(a) The quadratic is $x^2 - x - 2$.

The pair $1, -2$ has sum -1 and product -2. Thus
$$x^2 - x - 2 = (x + 1)(x - 2).$$
(Check: Multiplying out the brackets gives
$$(x + 1)(x - 2) = x^2 - 2x + x - 2$$
$$= x^2 - x - 2.)$$

(b) The quadratic is $u^2 + 4u - 12$.

The factor pairs of -12 are
$$-1, 12, \quad -2, 6, \quad -3, 4,$$
$$1, -12, \quad 2, -6, \quad 3, -4.$$
The only pair whose sum is 4 is $-2, 6$. Thus
$$u^2 + 4u - 12 = (u - 2)(u + 6).$$
(Check: Multiplying out the brackets gives
$$(u - 2)(u + 6) = u^2 + 6u - 2u - 12$$
$$= u^2 + 4u - 12.)$$

Activity 20

(a) $x^2 - x = x(x - 1)$

(b) $u^2 - 16 = u^2 - 4^2 = (u - 4)(u + 4)$

(c) $t^2 - 9t = t(t - 9)$

(d) $x^2 + 10x + 25 = (x + 5)^2$

Activity 21

(a) The equation is: $x^2 + 3x + 2 = 0$

Factorise: $(x + 1)(x + 2) = 0$

So: $x + 1 = 0$ or $x + 2 = 0$

So: $x = -1$ or $x = -2$

(Check: When $x = -1$,
$$x^2 + 3x + 2 = (-1)^2 + 3 \times (-1) + 2$$
$$= 1 - 3 + 2 = 0.$$
When $x = -2$,
$$x^2 + 3x + 2 = (-2)^2 + 3 \times (-2) + 2$$
$$= 4 - 6 + 2 = 0.)$$

(b) The equation is: $x^2 - 10x + 24 = 0$

Factorise: $(x - 4)(x - 6) = 0$

So: $x - 4 = 0$ or $x - 6 = 0$

So: $x = 4$ or $x = 6$

(Check: When $x = 4$,
$$x^2 - 10x + 24 = 4^2 - 10 \times 4 + 24$$
$$= 16 - 40 + 24 = 0.$$
When $x = 6$,
$$x^2 - 10x + 24 = 6^2 - 10 \times 6 + 24$$
$$= 36 - 60 + 24 = 0.)$$

(c) The equation is: $t^2 - 16 = 0$

Factorise: $\qquad (t - 4)(t + 4) = 0$

So: $\qquad\qquad t - 4 = 0 \quad$ or $\quad t + 4 = 0$

So: $\qquad\qquad t = 4 \quad$ or $\quad t = -4$

(Check: When $t = 4$,

$\quad t^2 - 16 = 4^2 - 16 = 16 - 16 = 0.$

When $t = -4$,

$\quad t^2 - 16 = (-4)^2 - 16 = 16 - 16 = 0.)$

(Factorising is not the best way to solve this equation. It is quicker to rearrange it as $t^2 = 16$ and take square roots.)

(d) The equation is: $u^2 - u - 12 = 0$

Factorise: $\qquad (u - 4)(u + 3) = 0$

So: $\qquad\qquad u - 4 = 0 \quad$ or $\quad u + 3 = 0$

So: $\qquad\qquad u = 4 \quad$ or $\quad u = -3$

(Check: When $u = 4$,

$\quad u^2 - u - 12 = 4^2 - 4 - 12$

$\qquad\qquad\qquad = 16 - 4 - 12 = 0.$

When $u = -3$,

$\quad u^2 - u - 12 = (-3)^2 - (-3) - 12$

$\qquad\qquad\qquad = 9 + 3 - 12 = 0.)$

(e) The equation is: $x^2 - 6x + 9 = 0$

Factorise: $\qquad (x - 3)(x - 3) = 0$

So: $\qquad\qquad x - 3 = 0$

So: $\qquad\qquad x = 3$

(Check: When $x = 3$,

$\quad x^2 - 6x + 9 = 3^2 - 6 \times 3 + 9$

$\qquad\qquad\qquad = 9 - 18 + 9 = 0.)$

(f) The equation is: $x^2 - 9x = 0$

Factorise: $\qquad x(x - 9) = 0$

So: $\qquad\qquad x = 0 \quad$ or $\quad x - 9 = 0$

So: $\qquad\qquad x = 0 \quad$ or $\quad x = 9$

(Check: When $x = 0$,

$\quad x^2 - 9x = 0^2 - 9 \times 0 = 0 - 0 = 0.$

When $x = 9$,

$\quad x^2 - 9x = 9^2 - 9 \times 9 = 81 - 81 = 0.)$

Activity 22

(a) In this case 3 is a factor of each of the coefficients, so

$$3x^2 - 3x - 36 = 3(x^2 - x - 12)$$
$$= 3(x - 4)(x + 3).$$

(b) In this case -5 is a factor of each of the coefficients, so

$$-5x^2 + 15x - 10 = -5(x^2 - 3x + 2)$$
$$= -5(x - 1)(x - 2).$$

Activity 23

(a) The quadratic expression is $2x^2 - 5x + 3$.

You can use the first method to look for a possible factorisation of the form

$$2x^2 - 5x + 3 = (2x\underline{\quad})(x\underline{\quad}).$$

The integers in the gaps must multiply together to give 3, and the possible factor pairs of 3 are

$$1, 3, \quad -1, -3.$$

These two factor pairs lead to four possible cases:

$$(2x + 1)(x + 3) \quad \text{or} \quad (2x + 3)(x + 1),$$
$$(2x - 1)(x - 3) \quad \text{or} \quad (2x - 3)(x - 1).$$

By multiplying out each of these pairs of brackets in turn, we find that one of these cases gives the required factorisation, specifically,

$$(2x - 3)(x - 1) = 2x^2 - 5x + 3.$$

(b) The quadratic expression is $6x^2 + 7x - 3$.

You can use the first method to look for possible factorisations of the form

$$6x^2 + 7x - 3 = (6x\underline{\quad})(x\underline{\quad})$$

or

$$6x^2 + 7x - 3 = (3x\underline{\quad})(2x\underline{\quad}).$$

The integers in the gaps must multiply together to give -3, and the possible factor pairs of -3 are

$$1, -3, \quad -1, 3.$$

These two factor pairs and the two possible factorisations lead to 8 possible cases:

$$(6x + 1)(x - 3) \quad \text{or} \quad (6x - 3)(x + 1),$$
$$(6x - 1)(x + 3) \quad \text{or} \quad (6x + 3)(x - 1),$$
$$(3x + 1)(2x - 3) \quad \text{or} \quad (3x - 3)(2x + 1),$$
$$(3x - 1)(2x + 3) \quad \text{or} \quad (3x + 3)(2x - 1).$$

By multiplying out each of these pairs of brackets in turn, we find that one of these cases gives the required factorisation, namely,

$$(3x - 1)(2x + 3) = 6x^2 + 7x - 3.$$

(c) The quadratic expression is $8x^2 - 10x - 3$.

You can use the second method to find a factorisation.

First find two numbers whose product is $ac = 8 \times (-3) = -24$ and whose sum is $b = -10$. The possible factor pairs of -24 (excluding those involving 24 or -24) are

$$-2, 12, \quad 2, -12, \quad -3, 8, \quad 3, -8, \quad -4, 6, \quad 4, -6.$$

Now choose a factor pair whose sum is -10. The only such pair is $2, -12$.

Next rewrite the quadratic expression, splitting the middle term $-10x$ into two terms using the factor pair $2, -12$, as follows:

$$8x^2 - 10x - 3 = 8x^2 + 2x - 12x - 3.$$

The required factorisation of $8x^2 - 10x - 3$ can now be obtained by taking out common factors:

$$8x^2 - 10x - 3 = \underbrace{8x^2 + 2x}\ \underbrace{- 12x - 3}$$
$$= 2x(4x + 1) - 3(4x + 1)$$
$$= (2x - 3)(4x + 1).$$

So

$$8x^2 - 10x - 3 = (2x - 3)(4x + 1).$$

Activity 24

(a) Since

$$2x^2 - 5x + 3 = (2x - 3)(x - 1),$$

the solutions of this equation satisfy

$$2x - 3 = 0 \quad \text{or} \quad x - 1 = 0,$$

so they are

$$x = \tfrac{3}{2} \quad \text{and} \quad x = 1.$$

(b) Since

$$6x^2 + 7x - 3 = (3x - 1)(2x + 3),$$

the solutions of this equation satisfy

$$3x - 1 = 0 \quad \text{or} \quad 2x + 3 = 0,$$

so they are

$$x = \tfrac{1}{3} \quad \text{and} \quad x = -\tfrac{3}{2}.$$

(c) Since

$$8x^2 - 10x - 3 = (2x - 3)(4x + 1),$$

the solutions of this equation satisfy

$$2x - 3 = 0 \quad \text{or} \quad 4x + 1 = 0,$$

so they are

$$x = \tfrac{3}{2} \quad \text{and} \quad x = -\tfrac{1}{4}.$$

Activity 25

(a) Since this is a right-angled triangle, the side lengths satisfy Pythagoras Theorem:

$$(x + 8)^2 = x^2 + (x + 7)^2.$$

(b) Expanding both brackets in the above equation gives

$$x^2 + 16x + 64 = x^2 + x^2 + 14x + 49$$
$$= 2x^2 + 14x + 49.$$

Subtracting $x^2 + 16x + 64$ from both sides gives $0 = x^2 - 2x - 15$, so x satisfies the quadratic equation

$$x^2 - 2x - 15 = 0.$$

Factorising gives

$$x^2 - 2x - 15 = (x - 5)(x + 3) = 0,$$

so the solutions of this quadratic equation satisfy

$$x - 5 = 0 \quad \text{or} \quad x + 3 = 0.$$

Hence

$$x = 5 \quad \text{or} \quad x = -3.$$

Since a negative number makes no sense as a solution, the answer must be $5\,\text{cm}$.

(Check: This gives sides of lengths $5\,\text{cm}$, $12\,\text{cm}$ and $13\,\text{cm}$, and the numbers 5, 12 and 13 do satisfy

$$13^2 = 169 = 5^2 + 12^2,$$

as required.)

Activity 26

The width of the garden is x metres and its length is $2x$ metres. Since the path is 1 metre wide, the dimensions of the rectangular lawn in metres are $x - 2$ wide and $2x - 2$ long. Hence

$$(x - 2)(2x - 2) = 40.$$

Expanding the brackets in this equation gives

$$2x^2 - 6x + 4 = 40,$$

so x satisfies the quadratic equation

$$2x^2 - 6x - 36 = 0; \quad \text{that is,} \quad x^2 - 3x - 18 = 0.$$

Factorising gives

$$x^2 - 3x - 18 = (x - 6)(x + 3) = 0,$$

so the solutions of this quadratic equation are

$$x = 6 \quad \text{and} \quad x = -3.$$

Since a negative number makes no sense as a solution, the garden must have width $6\,\text{m}$.

(Check: This gives width $6\,\text{m}$ and length $12\,\text{m}$ for the garden, so width $4\,\text{m}$ and length $10\,\text{m}$ for the lawn, and 4 and 10 do satisfy $4 \times 10 = 40$, as required.)

Activity 27

(a) $\dfrac{x^4}{x^9} = \dfrac{\overset{1}{\cancel{x^4}}}{\underset{x^5}{\cancel{x^9}}} = \dfrac{1}{x^5}$

(b) $\dfrac{20a^2b}{15ab^2} = \dfrac{\overset{4}{\cancel{20}}\,\overset{a}{\cancel{a^2}}\cancel{b}}{\underset{3}{\cancel{15}}\,\underset{1}{\cancel{a}}\,\underset{b}{\cancel{b^2}}} = \dfrac{4a}{3b}$

(c) $\dfrac{x^2 + 6x}{3x^2} = \dfrac{x(x + 6)}{3x^2} = \dfrac{\overset{1}{\cancel{x}}(x + 6)}{3\underset{x}{\cancel{x^2}}} = \dfrac{x + 6}{3x}$

(d) $\dfrac{u^2 - 4}{u^2 + 4u + 4} = \dfrac{(u - 2)(u + 2)}{(u + 2)^2}$

$$= \dfrac{(u - 2)\overset{1}{\cancel{(u + 2)}}}{\underset{u + 2}{\cancel{(u + 2)^2}}} = \dfrac{u - 2}{u + 2}$$

Activity 28

(a) $\dfrac{6}{y} + \dfrac{1}{y} = \dfrac{6+1}{y} = \dfrac{7}{y}$

(b) $\dfrac{x}{a^2} + \dfrac{y}{a^2} - \dfrac{z}{a^2} = \dfrac{x+y-z}{a^2}$

(c) Use $6xy$ as a common denominator:

$$\frac{a}{2x} - \frac{b}{3y} = \frac{3ay}{6xy} - \frac{2bx}{6xy} = \frac{3ay - 2bx}{6xy}.$$

(d) Use $3x(x+3)$ as a common denominator:

$$\frac{1}{3x} - \frac{2}{x+3} = \frac{x+3}{3x(x+3)} - \frac{6x}{3x(x+3)}$$
$$= \frac{x+3-6x}{3x(x+3)}$$
$$= \frac{-5x+3}{3x(x+3)}.$$

Activity 29

(a) Use x^4 as a common denominator:

$$\frac{5}{x^4} - \frac{4}{x^2} = \frac{5}{x^4} - \frac{4x^2}{x^4} = \frac{5-4x^2}{x^4}.$$

(b) Use $x(x+1)$ as a common denominator:

$$\frac{1}{x^2+x} - \frac{1}{x+1} = \frac{1}{x(x+1)} - \frac{x}{x(x+1)}$$
$$= \frac{1-x}{x(x+1)}.$$

(c) Use $b+3$ as a common denominator:

$$a + \frac{a}{b+3} = \frac{a}{1} + \frac{a}{b+3}$$
$$= \frac{a(b+3)}{b+3} + \frac{a}{b+3}$$
$$= \frac{a(b+3)+a}{b+3} = \frac{ab+4a}{b+3} = \frac{a(b+4)}{b+3}.$$

Activity 30

(a) $\dfrac{p^2}{q^2} \times \dfrac{p}{q} = \dfrac{p^2 \times p}{q^2 \times q} = \dfrac{p^3}{q^3}$

(b) $\dfrac{p^2}{q^2} \div \dfrac{p}{q} = \dfrac{p^2}{q^2} \times \dfrac{q}{p} = \dfrac{p^2 \times q}{q^2 \times p} = \dfrac{p^2 q}{q^2 p} = \dfrac{p}{q}$

(c) $\dfrac{9ax^2}{b} \times \dfrac{b^3}{4xy^2} = \dfrac{9ax^2 \times b^3}{b \times 4xy^2} = \dfrac{9axb^2}{4y^2}$

(d) $\dfrac{9ax^2}{b} \div \dfrac{b^3}{4xy^2} = \dfrac{9ax^2}{b} \times \dfrac{4xy^2}{b^3}$
$$= \frac{9ax^2 \times 4xy^2}{b \times b^3} = \frac{36ax^3y^2}{b^4}$$

(e) $8u^2 \times \dfrac{2}{u^2+u} = \dfrac{8u^2}{1} \times \dfrac{2}{u^2+u}$
$$= \frac{16u^2}{u^2+u} = \frac{16u^2}{u(u+1)} = \frac{16u}{u+1}$$

Activity 31

(a) By the rule for dividing by a fraction,

$$\frac{F}{f} = \frac{GM}{R^2} \div \frac{Gm}{r^2} = \frac{GM}{R^2} \times \frac{r^2}{Gm} = \frac{Mr^2}{mR^2}.$$

(b) We substitute $M = 80m$ and $R = 4r$ in the formula obtained in part (a):

$$\frac{F}{f} = \frac{80mr^2}{m(4r)^2} = \frac{80mr^2}{16mr^2} = 5,$$

so $F = 5f$.

Activity 32

(a) The equation is

$$\frac{4}{x-3} = \frac{12}{x+1}.$$

First multiply by $(x-3)(x+1)$ (assuming that $x \neq 3$ and $x \neq -1$):

$$(x-3)(x+1)\frac{4}{x-3} = (x-3)(x+1)\frac{12}{x+1}.$$

Then cancel and multiply out the brackets:

$$4(x+1) = 12(x-3);$$

that is,

$$4x+4 = 12x-36.$$

Finally, rearrange the equation as

$$8x = 40.$$

This gives $x = 5$ (which satisfies the assumptions).

(b) The equation is

$$\frac{t}{5} = \frac{2}{t+3}.$$

First multiply by $5(t+3)$ (assuming that $t \neq -3$):

$$5(t+3)\frac{t}{5} = 5(t+3)\frac{2}{t+3}.$$

Then cancel and multiply out the brackets:

$$t(t+3) = 10;$$

that is,

$$t^2 + 3t = 10.$$

Rearrange:

$$t^2 + 3t - 10 = 0.$$

Factorise:

$$(t+5)(t-2) = 0.$$

This gives $t = -5$ or $t = 2$ (which satisfy the assumptions).

(c) The equation is

$$\frac{4}{x} + 2x = 9.$$

First multiply by x (assuming that $x \neq 0$):

$$x\left(\frac{4}{x} + 2x\right) = 9x.$$

Then multiply out the brackets:

$$4 + 2x^2 = 9x.$$

Rearrange:

$$2x^2 - 9x + 4 = 0.$$

Factorise:

$$(2x - 1)(x - 4) = 0.$$

This gives $x = \frac{1}{2}$ or $x = 4$ (which satisfy the assumptions).

(d) The equation is

$$\frac{10}{x} + \frac{20}{x + 40} = \frac{1}{2}.$$

To clear all the fractions at once, multiply all terms by the product $2x(x + 40)$ of their denominators (assuming that $x \neq 0$ and $x \neq -40$):

$$2x(x + 40)\frac{10}{x} + 2x(x + 40)\frac{20}{x + 40} = 2x(x + 40)\frac{1}{2}.$$

Cancel:

$$20(x + 40) + 40x = x(x + 40).$$

Expand the brackets:

$$20x + 800 + 40x = x^2 + 40x.$$

Rearrange:

$$x^2 - 20x - 800 = 0.$$

Factorise:

$$(x - 40)(x + 20) = 0.$$

This gives $x = 40$ or $x = -20$ (which satisfy the assumptions).

Activity 33

(a) The equation is

$$v = \frac{2}{u + 3} + 4.$$

Multiply both sides by $u + 3$ (assuming that $u + 3 \neq 0$):

$$(u + 3)v = (u + 3)\left(\frac{2}{u + 3} + 4\right).$$

Multiply out brackets and cancel:

$$uv + 3v = 2 + 4(u + 3)$$
$$= 4u + 14.$$

Rearrange:

$$uv - 4u = 14 - 3v.$$

Factorise:

$$u(v - 4) = 14 - 3v.$$

Divide by $v - 4$ (assuming that $v - 4 \neq 0$):

$$u = \frac{14 - 3v}{v - 4}.$$

(b) The equation is

$$y = \frac{20}{3x} - \frac{3}{2}.$$

Multiply both sides by $6x$ (assuming that $x \neq 0$):

$$6xy = 6x\left(\frac{20}{3x} - \frac{3}{2}\right).$$

Multiply out the brackets and cancel:

$$6xy = 40 - 9x.$$

Rearrange:

$$6xy + 9x = 40.$$

Factorise:

$$x(6y + 9) = 40.$$

Divide by $6y + 9$ (assuming that $6y + 9 \neq 0$):

$$x = \frac{40}{6y + 9}.$$

Activity 34

(a) (i) The formula is

$$V = \tfrac{1}{3}\pi r^2 h.$$

Multiply by 3: $\qquad\qquad 3V = \pi r^2 h$

Divide by πh: $\qquad\qquad \dfrac{3V}{\pi h} = r^2$
(since $h \neq 0$)

Swap the sides: $\qquad\qquad r^2 = \dfrac{3V}{\pi h}$

Raise to the power $\frac{1}{2}$: $\qquad r = \left(\dfrac{3V}{\pi h}\right)^{\frac{1}{2}}$

(The last step is valid since the right-hand side is positive.)

(ii) If $h = 1\,\text{m}$ and $V = 2\,\text{m}^3$, then

$$r = \left(\frac{3 \times 2}{\pi \times 1}\right)^{\frac{1}{2}}$$
$$= 1.38\,\text{m} \text{ (to 3 s.f.)}$$

(b) The formula is

$$T^2 = \frac{MS^3}{cD}.$$

Multiply by cD (since $cD \neq 0$): $\quad cDT^2 = MS^3$

Divide by M (since $M \neq 0$): $\quad \dfrac{cDT^2}{M} = S^3$

Swap the sides: $\qquad\qquad S^3 = \dfrac{cDT^2}{M}$

Raise to the power $\frac{1}{3}$: $\qquad S = \left(\dfrac{cDT^2}{M}\right)^{\frac{1}{3}}$

(The last step is valid since the right-hand side is positive.)

Quadratics

Introduction

In Unit 6 you saw that many different real-life situations can be modelled by equations of the form

$$y = mx + c,$$

where m and c are constants. The graphs of equations of this form are straight lines, so models based on this type of equation are called *linear models*.

This unit is about equations of the form

$$y = ax^2 + bx + c, \tag{1}$$

where a, b and c are constants with $a \neq 0$. You will see some real-life situations that can be modelled by this type of equation. The right-hand side of an equation like this is a quadratic expression, so models like these are called *quadratic models*. The graphs of equations of this type have a characteristic curved shape called a *parabola*.

You will also learn some new methods of solving quadratic equations, which can be applied more generally than the method of factorisation that you learned in Unit 9.

The unit starts in Section 1 with some history about a quadratic model developed in the sixteenth century that provided an accurate means of predicting the motion of cannonballs. You will also see in this section that the vehicle stopping distances that you considered in Unit 2 arise from a quadratic model.

Section 2 explores the graphs of equations of form (1), and in Section 3 you will learn some new methods of solving quadratic equations and apply them to some quadratic models.

Section 4 presents a useful algebraic technique, called *completing the square*, that casts new light on the graphs of equations of form (1), and also provides an additional method for solving quadratic equations.

Finally, in Section 5, you will look at several more examples of quadratic models, from areas such as projectile motion, agriculture, economics and geometry. You will see in each case how the model can be used to solve a particular type of problem, called a *maximisation problem*, where the value of one quantity has to be chosen in order to obtain the maximum value of another quantity. An example of a maximisation problem is the problem of choosing what price to charge for goods or services in order to obtain the maximum revenue.

1 Introducing parabolas

Figure 1   Galileo Galilei (1564–1642) was an Italian astronomer, physicist and mathematician

In the sixteenth century, Galileo Galilei (Figure 1) studied the motion of objects moving under the force of gravity. This work led to important results that allowed him to accurately predict the paths of cannonballs – a useful skill in sixteenth-century Europe. In this section you will learn about some of Galileo's experiments and see how his results can be described using curves called *parabolas*. You will also revisit the topic of vehicle stopping distances, which was discussed in Unit 2.

1.1   Parabolas everywhere

You may have heard the story that Galileo dropped objects of different weights from the top of the Leaning Tower of Pisa, to disprove the commonly held belief that heavy objects fall faster than light objects. It is not known whether this story is true, but Galileo certainly conducted experiments on the motion of falling objects in his laboratory. This was difficult in the sixteenth century, because there were no devices that could accurately measure the short time that it took for an object to fall. Galileo's ingenious solution was to measure, instead, the time that a ball took to roll down a ramp, which is called an *inclined plane* by scientists. He reasoned that the motion of a rolling ball would be similar to that of a falling ball, but slower, enabling him to use the most accurate time-measuring device that he had at his disposal, a water clock.

Figure 2 shows a reconstruction of Galileo's laboratory. In the foreground is the inclined plane – a long sloping plank of wood with a groove on the top edge, down which a bronze ball was rolled.

Figure 2   A reconstruction of Galileo's laboratory at the Deutsches Museum, Munich

Galileo measured the time that the ball took to roll a certain distance from a stationary start, and found that in twice that time it would roll four times the distance, in three times the time it would roll nine times the distance, in four times the time it would roll sixteen times the distance, and so on. In general, if the time was multiplied by n, then the distance was multiplied by n^2. This was true for every angle of the inclined plane that he tried.

Galileo reasoned that this result should also hold for objects in *free fall*, that is, falling under the influence of gravity alone, because as the inclined plane becomes closer and closer to being vertical, the motion of the ball becomes closer and closer to free fall.

Today we have more sophisticated ways of measuring time and distance, and we do not have to 'slow down' the effects of gravity using an inclined plane as Galileo did. We can simply drop a ball and accurately measure the cumulative distance that it has fallen after each second.

Galileo's results are described in his book *Dialogue concerning two new sciences* (1638), as follows:

'We always found that the spaces traversed were to each other as the squares of the times and this was true for all inclinations of the plane.'

From a translation by Henry Crew and Alfonso de Salvio (1914).

Table 1 gives the approximate results that are obtained when this is done. The variables t and d represent the time that the ball has been falling in seconds and the distance that it has fallen in metres, respectively.

Table 1   The distance d (in metres)
fallen after time t (in seconds)

t	0	1	2	3	4
d	0	4.9	19.6	44.1	78.4

Figure 3 shows the points in Table 1 plotted on a graph, with time on the horizontal axis and distance on the vertical axis. The points are joined with a smooth curve.

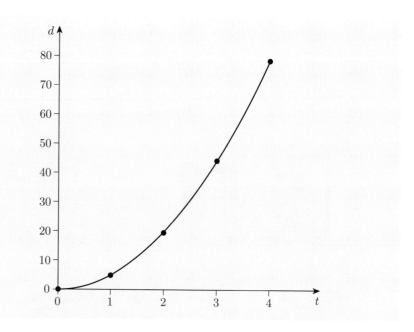

Figure 3   The distance d (in metres) fallen after time t (in seconds)

You met the idea of direct proportion in Unit 6.

The distance–time graph in Figure 3 is not a straight line, so the distance fallen by the ball is not proportional to the time that it has been falling – in other words, the ball does not fall at a constant speed. In fact, as you can see, the longer the ball has been falling, the greater the distance that it falls in a given time. For example, between 0 and 1 seconds the ball falls about 5 m, whereas between 1 and 2 seconds it falls about 15 m. So the ball speeds up as it falls – it *accelerates*. The continual increase in the speed of the ball gives the characteristic curved shape of the graph.

Because the graph of the distance fallen by the ball against the time that it has been falling is not a straight line, the relationship between these two quantities cannot be described by an equation of the type that you saw in Unit 6. However, it can be described by a different kind of equation.

You can see from the numbers in Table 1 that the relationship between the time taken and the distance fallen seems to be just as Galileo described:

in 1 second the ball falls 4.9 metres;
in 2 seconds it falls 19.6 metres, which is 4.9×2^2 metres;
in 3 seconds it falls 44.1 metres, which is 4.9×3^2 metres;
in 4 seconds it falls 78.4 metres, which is 4.9×4^2 metres.

So it seems that in general the relationship between d and t is expressed by the equation

$$d = 4.9t^2. \tag{2}$$

In other words, the distances are proportional to the *squares* of the times, with constant of proportionality 4.9. (This number depends on the fact that the units are metres and seconds.)

From the work of Isaac Newton (Figure 4), a hundred years after Galileo's experiments, it is known that the constant of proportionality in equation (2) is half of the value of the acceleration due to gravity. You learned in Unit 4 that the acceleration due to gravity varies slightly depending on where you are on Earth, but has the approximate value $9.81 \, \text{m/s}^2$ (to two decimal places). In this unit the acceleration due to gravity is taken to have the slightly less precise value of $9.8 \, \text{m/s}^2$. Elsewhere you might see the even less precise value of $10 \, \text{m/s}^2$ used.

Equation (2) is known as the **free-fall equation**, and it is often written in the form below, in which the acceleration due to gravity is represented by the letter g.

Figure 4 Isaac Newton (1643–1727)

The free-fall equation

The relationship between the distance d fallen by an object and the time t that it has been falling is given by

$$d = \tfrac{1}{2}gt^2,$$

where the constant g is the acceleration due to gravity, which is about $9.8 \, \text{m/s}^2$.

If the constant g is expressed in m/s^2, as here, then the variables t and d must be expressed in matching units, namely seconds and metres, respectively.

The curved shape of the graph of the free-fall equation is part of a curve that comes from a special family of curves, called **parabolas**. Some examples of parabolas are shown in Figure 5.

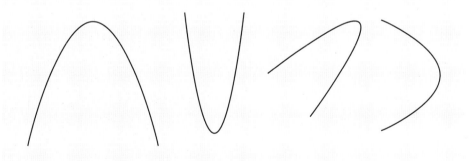

All the parabolas in the rest of the unit have a *vertical* line of symmetry, like the first two parabolas in Figure 5.

Figure 5 Four parabolas

A curve whose shape is all or part of a parabola is said to be **parabolic**. You have probably seen some examples of parabolic curves in your everyday life. A jet of water in a fountain forms a parabola, as does the path of an object that is thrown – you will learn more about this in the next subsection. The reflecting mirror in a torch or car headlight has a cross-section that is a parabola, because this shape of mirror gathers up light from a source and projects it in one direction as a beam. The same shape of reflector also does the opposite; that is, it reflects incoming rays towards a single point. For this reason the cross-section of a satellite dish is a parabola – the dish reflects signals towards a receiver. Figure 6 shows some examples of parabolas and parabolic reflectors.

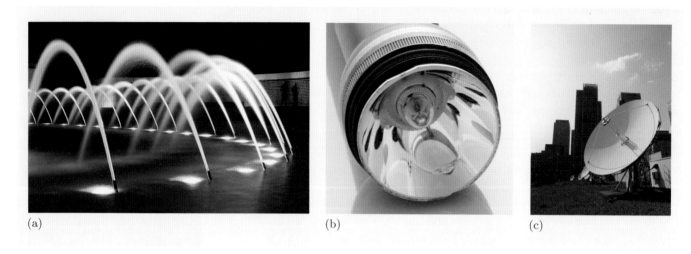

(a) (b) (c)

Figure 6   (a) A fountain, (b) the reflector in a torch and (c) a satellite dish

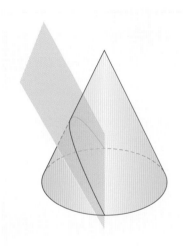

Figure 7   The intersection of a cone and a plane parallel to its side gives a parabola

There are various ways to describe the shape of a parabola, but all the descriptions give the same family of curves. For example, a parabola is the shape obtained when a plane 'parallel' to the side of a cone intersects the cone, as shown in Figure 7. Strictly, the cone should be an 'infinite' cone, as the two ends of a parabola are infinitely long. Alternatively, a parabola is the shape of the graph of any equation of the form

$$y = \boxed{\text{a quadratic expression in } x} .$$

That is,

$$y = ax^2 + bx + c, \tag{3}$$

where a, b and c are constants with $a \neq 0$. The free-fall equation has this form, with $a = 4.9$ and $b = c = 0$, and the variables t and d instead of x and y. You will learn much more about parabolas and their equations throughout this unit.

> The word 'parabola' was first used for curves like those in Figure 5 by the Greek geometer and astronomer Apollonius, in around 200 BC, though the shape itself was discovered even earlier. The word means 'juxtaposition' or 'application' in Greek. Later writers thought this word appropriate because the plane shown in Figure 7 can be thought of as being 'juxtaposed to' the cone – parallel to its side.

It is important to appreciate that the free-fall equation is only a *model* for the motion of a falling object. It is accurate if there are no forces other than gravity acting on the object, but in real life other forces do usually affect the motion, notably *air resistance*, which is sometimes called *drag*. Air resistance tends to slow down a falling object. If the object falls a great enough distance, then eventually air resistance will cause its speed to stop increasing and become constant – this constant speed is known as its *terminal velocity*. However, the effects of air resistance are negligible for compact objects falling reasonably short distances, such as the distances in Figure 3 on page 128, and the free-fall equation is a good model for the motion of such objects.

Any model based on an equation of form (3) is called a **quadratic model**.

If you want to know how long it would take for an object to fall a certain distance, then you may be able to read off an approximate answer from the graph of the free-fall equation. For example, the dashed red lines in Figure 8 show that an object would take about 3.8 seconds to fall 70 metres. Alternatively, you can find the answer by substituting into the free-fall equation. You are asked to do this in the first activity.

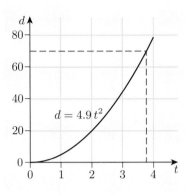

Figure 8 An object takes 3.8 seconds to fall 70 metres

Activity I   Using the free-fall equation

A ball is dropped out of a window at a height of 26 m. By substituting $d = 26$ into the free-fall equation, find the time that the ball takes to reach the ground, to the nearest tenth of a second.

Sometimes, instead of considering the distance that an object has fallen after a particular time, it is more convenient to consider its height above the ground after that time. The height of a falling object at any time is just the difference between its initial height and the distance that it has fallen, as shown in Figure 9.

For example, consider the ball dropped out of the window in Activity 1. Its initial height is 26 m, and the distance d metres that it has fallen after t seconds is given by the free-fall equation

$$d = 4.9t^2,$$

so its height h metres above the ground after t seconds is given by the equation

$$h = 26 - 4.9t^2. \qquad (4)$$

In the next activity you are asked to use Graphplotter to draw the graph of this equation and obtain a result about the motion of the ball.

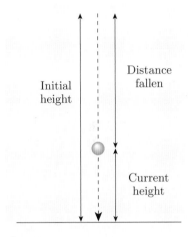

Figure 9 The height of a falling object

 Graphplotter

---

Activity 2   Plotting height against time for the ball

Use Graphplotter, with the 'One graph' tab selected.

(a) To obtain a graph of the equation

$$y = 26 - 4.9x^2,$$

which is equation (4) with t and h replaced by x and y, respectively, first choose the equation $y = ax^2 + bx + c$ from the drop-down list. Then set $a = -4.9$, $b = 0$ and $c = 26$, by typing these values into the boxes and pressing 'Enter'.

Decide on suitable minimum and maximum values for the x- and y-axes, and enter these values in the boxes at the bottom right of Graphplotter. The solution to Activity 1 will help you to choose a suitable maximum value for the x-axis.

(b) Use the Graphplotter graph to find, to the nearest metre, the height of the ball above the ground after 1.2 seconds. To do this, first click the tab for the 'Options' page, and ensure that 'Trace' is ticked and 'Coordinates' and 'y-intercept' are not ticked. Then type 1.2 into the box for the x-coordinate of the cursor (at the bottom left of the graph panel), press 'Enter' and look at the trace coordinates displayed on the graph.

Graphplotter only uses the variables x and y.

You can use the method in part (b) to find the y-coordinate on any graph corresponding to a given x-coordinate, but not the other way round. You will learn how to go the other way in Subsection 3.1.

1.2 Projectiles

A **projectile** is an object that is propelled through space by a force that ceases after launch, such as a ball that is thrown, or a cannonball that is fired from a cannon. The **trajectory** of a projectile is the path that it follows. The science of projectiles, especially those fired from firearms, is called **ballistics**.

In medieval times very little accurate information was known about the trajectories of cannonballs, but 'bombardiering', an old name for ballistics, was an increasingly important science for anyone who wanted a military advantage.

An effect due to air turbulence can sometimes cause a spinning object, such as a golf ball, to have a trajectory of roughly the shape shown in Figure 10(b).

Below you can see some guidance given to bombardiers in the sixteenth and seventeenth centuries to help them to hit their targets. In Figure 10(a) the trajectory of a cannonball is shown as consisting of two straight-line segments – one from the muzzle of the cannon to a point marked k on the diagram, and the other vertically downwards from this point to the ground. In Figure 10(b) the trajectory is described as having three phases – the 'violent motion', the 'mixt or crooked motion' and the 'naturall motion'.

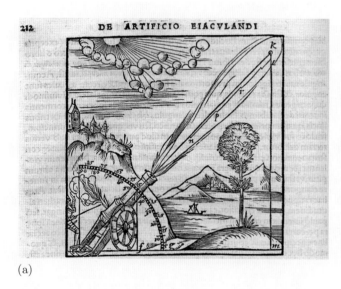

(a)

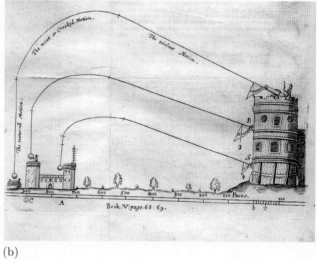

(b)

Figure 10 (a) Daniel Santbech, *Problematum astronomicorum et geometricorum sectiones septem* (Basel, 1561). (b) Samuel Sturmy, *The mariners magazine, or Sturmy's mathematical and practical arts* (first edition, 1669; this edition, London, 1684).

Galileo, a Florentine, was appointed to a professorship of mathematics at the University of Pisa in 1589, by Fernando, Duke of Tuscany. Much of Galileo's work on the military applications of mathematics was dedicated to him. The Duke's eldest son, Cosimo II, was taught mathematics by Galileo.

In fact, the author of the book from which Figure 10(b) is taken, Samuel Sturmy, was well behind the times. Galileo had progressed from his work on free-fall motion to experiments on the motion of projectiles, and his results were published in 1638, in the same book in which he discussed his free-fall experiments, *Dialogue concerning two new sciences*.

In his projectile experiments, Galileo continued to use the inclined plane that he had used in his free-fall experiments, but he added a horizontal shelf at the end of the slope, at a height above the floor, so that the ball was launched horizontally into the air. A similar set-up is illustrated in Figure 11.

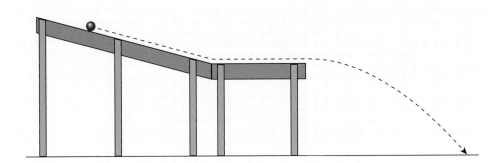

Figure II   Galileo's projectile experiment

Galileo rolled an inked ball down the inclined plane and recorded the position on the floor where it landed. By starting the ball at different heights along the inclined plane, he could vary the speed with which the ball left the shelf, resulting in different trajectories. Figure 12 shows some trajectories that Galileo sketched in his laboratory notebook.

Galileo found that the motion of the ball could be understood by thinking about its vertical motion and its horizontal motion separately. At any given time after the ball leaves the shelf, its vertical distance from the end of the shelf, as shown in Figure 13, is determined by the free-fall equation $d = \frac{1}{2}gt^2$, just as if it were falling vertically. At the same time, its horizontal distance from the end of the shelf is determined by the constant speed equation $d = st$, where s is the speed with which the ball leaves the shelf, just as if it were travelling horizontally at that constant speed. The position of the ball at any time is a combination of its horizontal and vertical distances. The different positions of the ball after leaving the shelf give the shape of its trajectory.

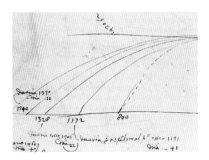

Figure I2   Part of a page from Galileo's notebooks

Here are Galileo's findings, from a translation of *Dialogue concerning two new sciences*:

'The moving particle, which we imagine to be a heavy one, will on passing over the edge of the plane acquire, in addition to its previous uniform and perpetual motion, a downward propensity due to its own weight; so that the resulting motion which I call projection is compounded of one which is uniform and horizontal and of another which is vertical and naturally accelerated'.

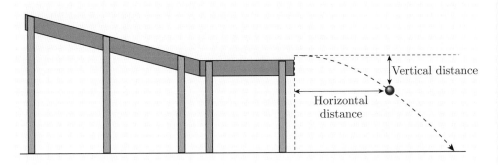

Figure I3   The vertical and horizontal distances of the ball from the shelf

The motion of any projectile launched horizontally, like the inked ball in Galileo's experiments, can be predicted by using the description above. Of course, as with the free-fall equation, this description is just a model, and in real life forces such as air resistance cause the motion of a horizontally-launched projectile to differ to some extent from that predicted by the model.

Figure 14   A cannon from the Alderney being recovered from the sea

Figure 15   A replica of one of the Alderney cannons being fired

In the example below, the model is used to predict the distance travelled by an Elizabethan cannonball fired horizontally. To make the prediction, an estimate for the speed with which a cannonball would have left the muzzle of an Elizabethan cannon is needed.

In 2008, two cannons from an Elizabethan ship known as the Alderney were recovered from the sea off the Channel Islands. The ship is thought to have sunk in 1592, just four years after the defeat of the Spanish Armada, so it is likely that it took part in that great sea battle. A replica was made of one of the cannons, and it was found, much to everyone's surprise, that the maximum muzzle speed was close to the speed of sound, which is about 340 m/s.

Example 1   *Predicting the range of a cannonball*

Suppose that a cannon is fired horizontally from the upper deck of a ship 10 m above the sea, and that the cannonball leaves the muzzle with a speed of 300 m/s.

(a) Calculate the time in seconds that the cannonball will take to hit the sea.

(b) Hence calculate the horizontal distance in metres that the cannonball will travel before hitting the sea.

Give your answers to two significant figures.

Solution

(a) The time t seconds for the cannonball to hit the sea is given by the free-fall equation

$$d = 4.9t^2,$$

where d is the vertical distance in metres between the cannon and the sea, that is, $d = 10$.

Substituting into the equation and solving it gives

$$10 = 4.9t^2$$
$$4.9t^2 = 10$$
$$t^2 = \frac{10}{4.9}$$
$$t = \sqrt{\frac{10}{4.9}} = 1.428\ldots = 1.4 \text{ (to 2 s.f.)}.$$

(The positive square root is taken because the negative one does not make sense in this context.)

So the cannonball will hit the sea after about 1.4 s.

(b) The horizontal distance that the cannonball will travel before hitting the sea is given by the equation $d = st$, where s is the speed with which the cannonball leaves the cannon, and t is the time that it travels before hitting the sea. So $s = 300$ and, from part (a), $t = 1.428\ldots$, where the units are metres per second and seconds, respectively.

Substituting into the equation gives

$$d = 300 \times 1.428\ldots = 430 \text{ (to 2 s.f.)}.$$

So the cannonball will travel for about 430 m before hitting the sea.

Here is a similar activity for you to try.

Activity 3 *Predicting the range of a projectile*

Suppose that a marble is rolled off the edge of a horizontal tabletop with a speed of $0.5\,\text{m/s}$. The tabletop is $0.8\,\text{m}$ above the floor.

(a) Calculate the time in seconds that the marble will take to hit the floor.

(b) Calculate the horizontal distance in metres that the marble will travel before hitting the floor.

Give your answers to two significant figures.

A striking consequence of the description of the motion of a horizontally-launched projectile that you saw on page 133 is that if you fire a bullet horizontally from a gun across unobstructed level ground, and drop a bullet from the same height at the same time, then the two bullets will hit the ground at the same time.

Galileo realised that the trajectory of a horizontally-launched projectile predicted by his model is parabolic. To see why this is, consider, for example, the trajectory of the marble in Activity 3. Think of the trajectory as a curve on a graph, as shown in Figure 16.

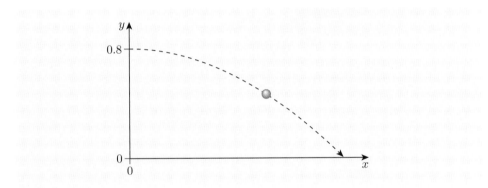

Figure 16 The trajectory of the marble viewed as a graph

For each point on the curve, the x-coordinate is the horizontal distance travelled by the marble after a particular time, and the y-coordinate is its height above the floor at that time, where both measurements are in metres.

Since the initial horizontal speed of the marble is $0.5\,\text{m/s}$, after t seconds the marble has travelled the horizontal distance $0.5t$ metres. The height of the marble at this time is the height of the table minus the distance that the marble has fallen, that is, $0.8 - 4.9t^2$ metres. So, at time t,

$$x = 0.5t \quad \text{and} \quad y = 0.8 - 4.9t^2.$$

Let's express y in terms of x, so that we can see whether this gives a formula of the form

$$y = \boxed{\text{a quadratic expression in } x}\ .$$

You can express y in terms of x by first expressing t in terms of x and then substituting this expression into the equation for y. Since $x = 0.5t$, we have $t = x/0.5$, that is, $t = 2x$. Substituting this into the equation for y gives

$$y = 0.8 - 4.9(2x)^2.$$

Simplifying gives

$$y = 0.8 - 19.6x^2.$$

This formula is of the form

$$y = ax^2 + bx + c,$$

with $a = -19.6$, $b = 0$ and $c = 0.8$. So the curve is indeed part of a parabola. Any trajectory given by Galileo's model for the motion of a horizontally-launched projectile can be shown to be parabolic in the same way.

Galileo went on to look at projectiles launched at various angles, which allowed him to make predictions about the trajectories of cannonballs fired at different angles. He found that the trajectories of projectiles were always parabolic, and by the beginning of the eighteenth century this knowledge was being incorporated into military handbooks, as Figure 17 shows.

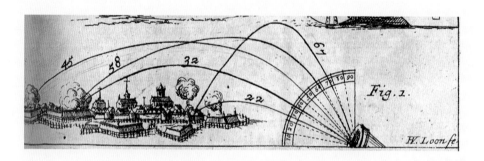

Figure 17   Nicolas Bion, *Traitè de la construction et des principaux usages des instrumens de mathematique* (Paris, 1709)

The diagram in Figure 17 indicates that the maximum range of a cannon is achieved when the cannonball is fired at an angle of 45 degrees, and that there are two possible angles that can be used to hit any closer target.

1.3 Stopping distances

In this subsection you will see that the stopping distances given in the Highway Code, which were considered in Unit 2, arise from a quadratic model.

Stopping distances were first included in the third edition of the Highway Code, published in 1946, and they remained essentially unchanged in all subsequent editions, at least up to the time of writing of MU123. Imperial units were predominant in 1946, so the stopping distances were given in feet, with the vehicle speeds in miles per hour. As now, each stopping distance was made up of two parts, the thinking distance and the braking distance, as you can see from Table 2.

Figure 18   The cover of the third edition (1946) of the Highway Code

Table 2   The thinking, braking and stopping distances published in the third edition (1946) of the Highway Code

Speed (mph)	Thinking distance (feet)	Braking distance (feet)	Overall stopping distance (feet)
10	10	5	15
20	20	20	40
30	30	45	75
40	40	80	120
50	50	125	175

The thinking distances in Table 2 are based on a linear model. If s is the vehicle speed in miles per hour and T is the thinking distance in feet, then, as you can see, T is given by the simple formula

$$T = s.$$

The braking distances are based on a quadratic model. If s is the vehicle speed in miles per hour, as before, and B is the braking distance in feet, then B is given by the formula

$$B = \tfrac{1}{20}s^2. \tag{5}$$

Activity 4   *Checking the formula for the braking distances*

Choose one of the speeds given in Table 2, and calculate the corresponding braking distance given by formula (5). Check that your answer is the same as the braking distance given in the table.

The expressions for the thinking distances and the braking distances can be added together to give a formula for the overall stopping distances. This formula is

$$D = \tfrac{1}{20}s^2 + s, \tag{6}$$

where s is the vehicle speed in miles per hour and D is the overall stopping distance in feet. So the overall stopping distances are also given by a quadratic model and hence they lie on a parabolic curve.

The graph of formula (6) is shown in Figure 19, with the points given by the numbers in Table 2 marked on the curve.

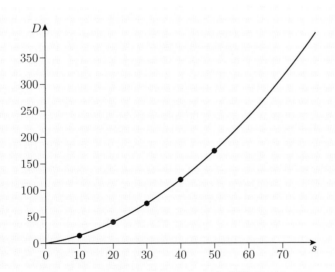

Figure 19   The graph of the formula $D = \tfrac{1}{20}s^2 + s$

Figure 20 shows the stopping distances given in the 2007 version of the Highway Code. They are the same as those in Table 2, with small differences arising from rounding when the thinking and braking distances are converted to metres. The 2007 version gives a different range of speeds – it covers 20 mph to 70 mph, whereas the 1946 version covers 10 mph to 50 mph – but the stopping distances for 60 mph and 70 mph are also given by formula (6), as you might like to check.

Typical Stopping Distances

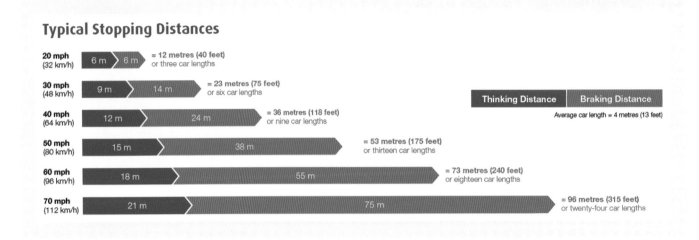

Figure 20

In this section you have read about the experiments that Galileo carried out in order to investigate the motion of objects in free fall and the trajectories of projectiles, and you have learned more about vehicle stopping distances. You saw that the distance–time graph of free-fall motion, the trajectory of a projectile and the graph that models vehicle stopping distances are all parabolic curves.

2 Graphs of quadratic functions

In Section 1 you learned that the graph of an equation of the form

$$y = ax^2 + bx + c, \tag{7}$$

where a, b and c are constants with $a \neq 0$, has a shape called a *parabola*. In this section you will explore the different shapes of parabolas obtained by plotting graphs of this form, and the different positions of these parabolas relative to the axes.

One feature that you will see is that every parabola has a line of symmetry, as shown in Figure 21. Another name for a line of symmetry is an **axis of symmetry**, and this is the phrase that is usually used when discussing parabolas. The axis of symmetry of a parabola cuts the parabola at exactly one point. This point is called the **vertex** of the parabola, also shown in Figure 21.

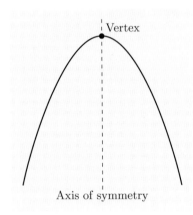

Figure 21 The axis of symmetry and vertex of a parabola

This section also uses the following terminology, which you met in Unit 6. Whenever you have an equation that expresses one variable in terms of another variable, you can think of it as a rule that takes an input value and produces an output value. For example, if the equation is $y = x^2$, then inputting $x = 3$ gives the output $y = 9$, inputting $x = -1$ gives $y = 1$, and so on. A rule that takes input values and produces output values like this is called a **function**.

A function whose rule is of the form $y = ax^2 + bx + c$, where a, b and c are constants with $a \neq 0$, is called a **quadratic function**. So this section is about the graphs of quadratic functions.

2.1 Graphs of equations of the form $y = ax^2$

We begin by looking at the graphs obtained when the constants b and c in equation (7) are both zero, that is, when the equation has the form

$$y = ax^2, \quad \text{where } a \neq 0.$$

For example, the equations

$$y = 2x^2, \quad y = x^2 \quad \text{and} \quad y = -x^2$$

are of this form, with a equal to 2, 1 and -1, respectively.

We begin by looking at the simple equation

$$y = x^2.$$

You can plot a graph of this equation by constructing a table of values, in the way that you saw in Unit 6. You choose some appropriate values for x, and calculate the corresponding values of y by substituting into the equation. You can choose both positive and negative values of x, and Table 3 shows some results obtained in this way.

Table 3 A table of values for the equation $y = x^2$

x	-3	-2	-1	0	1	2	3
y	9	4	1	0	1	4	9

Notice the symmetry in the y-values in Table 3: the values decrease until they reach 0, and then they increase again in the same steps. This happens because $(-x)^2 = x^2$, for any x.

If you plot the seven points given by Table 3 and join them with a smooth curve, then you obtain the graph in Figure 22.

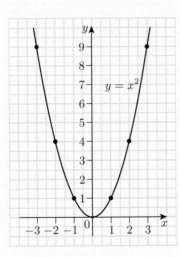

Figure 22 The graph of $y = x^2$

Notice that the curve in Figure 22 has a line of symmetry (the y-axis), as expected. This is because of the symmetry of the y-values.

In the next activity you are asked to plot the graph of another simple quadratic function.

Remember that $-x^2$ means the negative of the square of x, not the square of the negative of x. For example,

$-3^2 = -9$ (not 9).

(A minus sign indicating a negative has the same precedence in the BIDMAS rules as a minus sign indicating subtraction.)

Activity 5   Plotting the graph of $y = -x^2$

(a) By constructing a table of values, plot the graph of the equation $y = -x^2$.

(b) Compare your graph to the graph of $y = x^2$ in Figure 22, and write a sentence or two to explain what you see.

In Activity 5 you saw that the graphs of $y = ax^2$ when $a = 1$ and when $a = -1$ are exactly the same shape, but mirror images of each other, reflected in the x-axis. This is because changing a from 1 to -1 in the equation $y = ax^2$ changes all the y-values to their negatives, as you can see if you compare Table 3 to the table in the solution to Activity 5.

The same thing happens for any value of a: if you change the value of a to its negative, then all the y-values obtained from the equation $y = ax^2$ change to their negatives, so the parabola changes to its mirror image, reflected in the x-axis.

In the next activity you are asked to use Graphplotter to investigate the graph of the equation $y = ax^2$ for some more values of a, both positive and negative.

 Graphplotter

Activity 6   Exploring the graph of $y = ax^2$

(a) First use Graphplotter with the 'One graph' tab selected. Choose the equation $y = ax^2 + bx + c$ from the drop-down list. Set b and c to 0, and keep them set to 0 throughout this activity, since the aim is to explore the graph of $y = ax^2$.

Set a to 1, and check that you obtain the graph shown in Figure 22 on page 139. Now use the slider to increase the value of a, and then to decrease it again, but only within positive values of a. What is the effect on the shape of the graph as you change the value of a?

(b) Now choose the 'Two graphs' tab in Graphplotter. Choose the equation $y = ax^2 + bx + c$ from both drop-down lists, and check that b and c are set to 0 for both graphs.

Set a to 1 and -1 for the first and second graphs, respectively, and check that the graphs are reflections of each other in the x-axis, as expected. Try some other pairs of values of a that are negatives of each other, and check that the graphs are as you expect. You might also like to use the slider to see how the graph changes as a changes within the negative values.

The magnitude of a number is sometimes called its *size*, and this was the word used in Unit 6. For example, the magnitude of -3 is 3, and the magnitude of 3 is also 3.

You should have found in Activity 6 that the value of a appears to affect how narrow the graph of $y = ax^2$ is. More specifically, it is the *magnitude* of a that affects the width of the graph – the **magnitude** of a number is its value without its negative sign, if it has one. The larger the magnitude of a, the narrower the parabola becomes.

To see why this is, think of a point, other than $(0, 0)$, on the graph of $y = x^2$, say. Now imagine changing the graph to make it the graph of $y = 2x^2$. The point with the same x-value now has a y-value twice as large, so it has moved up. All the points on the parabola except $(0, 0)$ move up in this way. The further away they are from the vertex $(0,0)$, the larger their y-value is to start with, so the more they move up. This has the effect of making the parabola more narrow. Similarly, if you change $y = -x^2$ to $y = -2x^2$, then the points move down, so again the parabola becomes narrower. The axis of symmetry of the graph is not affected.

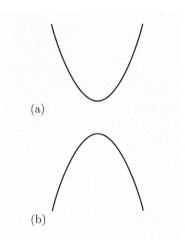

(a)

(b)

Figure 23 (a) A u-shaped parabola (b) An n-shaped parabola

Because the point $(0,0)$ on the parabola does not move when you change the value of a, the vertex of the parabola does not change. So for all values of a, the vertex of the graph of $y = ax^2$ is at the origin.

Another property that you saw in Activity 6 is that, as expected, if a is positive, then the graph of $y = ax^2$ is the same way up as the graph of $y = x^2$, while if a is negative, then it is the other way up. A parabola that is the same way up as the graph of $y = x^2$ is called a **u-shaped** parabola, while one that is the other way up is called an **n-shaped** parabola. These two possibilities are illustrated in Figure 23.

Here is a summary of what you have learned about the graphs of equations of the form $y = ax^2$ in this subsection.

> **The graph of the equation** $y = ax^2$
>
> The vertex is $(0,0)$.
>
> If a is positive, then the graph is u-shaped.
>
> If a is negative, then the graph is n-shaped.
>
> The larger the magnitude of a, the narrower the parabola.

2.2 Graphs of equations of the form $y = ax^2 + bx + c$

In this subsection you will explore the graphs of general quadratic functions.

In the first activity you are asked to explore the graphs that are obtained when the coefficient c in the equation $y = ax^2 + bx + c$ is zero. That is, you will explore the graphs of equations of the form

$$y = ax^2 + bx.$$

Activity 7 *Graphs of equations of the form $y = ax^2 + bx$*

Graphplotter

Use Graphplotter, with the 'One graph' tab selected.

(a) Choose the equation $y = ax^2 + bx + c$ from the drop-down list. Set $a = 1$, $b = 0$ and $c = 0$, and check that you obtain the graph of $y = x^2$, as expected.

(b) Now explore the effect of changing the value of b. Notice that although the position of the vertex changes, the following features of the graph remain the same:

- its shape
- the fact that its axis of symmetry is vertical
- which way up it is
- the fact that it goes through $(0,0)$.

(c) Repeat part (b) for one or two other values of a.

In Activity 7 you should have found that for all values of a and b that you tried, the graph of $y = ax^2 + bx$ is exactly the same as the graph of $y = ax^2$, but shifted to a different position relative to the axes. The word 'shifted' here means that the parabola is just slid to a new position – it is not rotated in any way, so its axis of symmetry remains vertical.

You should also have found that for all values of a and b that you tried, the graph of $y = ax^2 + bx$ passes through the point $(0, 0)$. This is because substituting $x = 0$ in the equation $y = ax^2 + bx$ gives $y = 0$.

In the next activity you are asked to look at the effect of changing the value of the constant term c in the equation $y = ax^2 + bx + c$.

Graphplotter

Activity 8   *Graphs of equations of the form* $y = ax^2 + bx + c$

Use Graphplotter, with the 'One graph' tab selected.

Make sure that 'y-intercept' in the Options page is ticked. This causes the coordinates of the point where the graph crosses the y-axis to be displayed.

(a) Choose the equation $y = ax^2 + bx + c$ from the drop-down list. Set $a = 1$, $b = 0$ and $c = 0$, and check that you obtain the graph of $y = x^2$, as expected.

(b) Now set $c = 1$. What is the effect on the graph? In particular, what is the point where it crosses the y-axis?

(c) Choose some other values of c (both positive and negative) and repeat part (b) for each of these values.

(d) Repeat parts (b) and (c) for some other values of a and b, and describe what you find.

In Activity 8 you should have found that for any values of a, b and c, the graph of $y = ax^2 + bx + c$ is exactly the same as the graph of $y = ax^2 + bx$, except that it is shifted vertically up or down, so that it crosses the y-axis at $(0, c)$ instead of $(0, 0)$.

This is because adding the constant c to the right-hand side of the equation $y = ax^2 + bx$ just changes all the y-values by c units, which causes the graph to move up or down.

So, from what you have seen in Activities 7 and 8, it seems that for all values of a, b and c, the graph of $y = ax^2 + bx + c$ is exactly the same shape as the graph of $y = ax^2$, but shifted horizontally and/or vertically to a different position relative to the axes. This is indeed the case, and you will see why later in the unit.

This means that the only possible basic shapes of parabolas are the shapes of the graphs of the form $y = ax^2$. You have seen that these all have a vertical axis of symmetry and differ in how wide they are.

In particular, the graph of the equation $y = ax^2 + bx + c$ is always a u-shaped or n-shaped parabola. If a is positive, then it is u-shaped; if a is negative, then it is n-shaped.

Here is a summary of what you have learned in this subsection about the graphs of quadratic functions.

> **The graph of the equation** $y = ax^2 + bx + c$
>
> If a is positive, then the graph is u-shaped.
>
> If a is negative, then the graph is n-shaped.
>
> The graph has the same shape as the graph of $y = ax^2$, but shifted.
>
> The graph crosses the y-axis at $(0, c)$.

Figure 24 A smile-shaped parabola goes with a positive coefficient of x^2, and a frown-shaped parabola goes with a negative coefficient of x^2

Figure 24 suggests a way to remember the relationship between the sign of the coefficient of x^2 and whether the graph is u-shaped or n-shaped.

2.3 The intercepts of a parabola

You met the idea of the *intercepts* of a graph in Unit 6. An **x-intercept** of a graph is a value where it crosses or touches the x-axis. In other words, it is a value of x for which $y = 0$. Similarly, a **y-intercept** of a graph is a value where it crosses or touches the y-axis. That is, it is a value of y for which $x = 0$. For example, the x-intercepts of the parabola shown in Figure 25 are -2 and 5, and the y-intercept is -10.

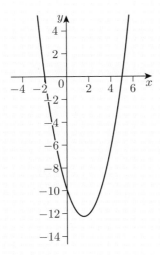

Figure 25 The graph of $y = x^2 - 3x - 10$

The graph of a quadratic function can have two, one or zero x-intercepts, depending on its position relative to the x-axis. The three possibilities are shown in Figure 26, for u-shaped parabolas.

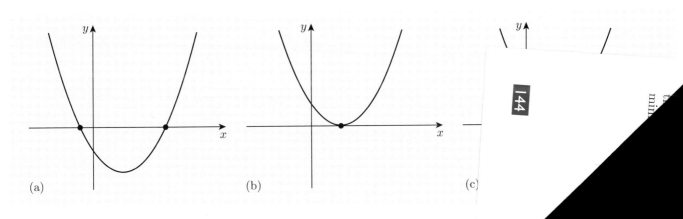

(a)   (b)   (c)

Figure 26 The graph of $y = ax^2 + bx + c$ can have two, one or zero x-inte

There is always exactly one y-intercept, because there is exactly one value of y for each value of x, including $x = 0$.

You can use the equation of a parabola to find its intercepts.

Finding the y-intercept

To obtain the y-intercept of a parabola, you substitute $x = 0$ into its equation. For example, consider the parabola with equation

$$y = x^2 - 3x - 10.$$

Substituting $x = 0$ into this equation gives $y = -10$, so the y-intercept of this parabola is -10, as shown in Figure 25.

Notice that whatever the values of a, b and c, if you substitute $x = 0$ into the equation $y = ax^2 + bx + c$, then you obtain $y = c$. So the y-intercept of the graph is always the value c, as was observed in the previous subsection.

Finding the x-intercepts

To obtain the x-intercepts of a parabola, you substitute $y = 0$ into the equation. For example, consider again the parabola with equation

$$y = x^2 - 3x - 10.$$

Substituting $y = 0$ gives

$$0 = x^2 - 3x - 10,$$

so the x-intercepts of the parabola are the solutions of this quadratic equation. The quadratic expression on the right-hand side factorises as $(x + 2)(x - 5)$, so the x-intercepts are -2 and 5, as shown in Figure 25.

Finding the x-intercepts of a parabola always involves solving a quadratic equation. If you cannot solve the equation by factorisation, then you may be able to solve it by using the *quadratic formula*, which you will meet in Section 3.

If the quadratic equation has only one solution, then the parabola has only one x-intercept. If it has no solutions at all, then the parabola has no x-intercepts. In Section 3 you will learn how to tell from the coefficients of a quadratic equation how many solutions it has.

You will have a chance to practise finding the intercepts of parabolas in the next subsection.

2.4 Sketch graphs of quadratic functions

When you are dealing with a quadratic function, it can be useful to have an idea of what its graph looks like. Often you do not need an accurate plot, but just a quick sketch showing some of the main features. The features that you would usually show on such a sketch are as follows:

In general, a sketch graph of a function should show its general shape and features such as its intercepts and any points where the curve reaches a maximum or imum.

- whether it is u-shaped or n-shaped

- its intercepts

- its axis of symmetry

- its vertex.

You have already seen how to determine whether a parabola is u-shaped or n-shaped from its equation, and how to find its intercepts.

You can find the axis of symmetry by using the fact that this line lies halfway between the x-intercepts, or passes through the single x-intercept if there is only one. You will see later in this subsection how you can find the axis of symmetry if there are no x-intercepts.

The equation of the axis of symmetry tells you the x-coordinate of the vertex, and you can substitute that into the equation of the parabola to find the corresponding y-coordinate.

The next example shows you how you might go about producing a sketch graph of a quadratic function.

Example 2   *Sketching the graph of a quadratic function*

Tutorial clip

This question is about the parabola
$$y = -x^2 + 2x + 8.$$

(a) State whether the parabola is u-shaped or n-shaped, and find its intercepts.

(b) Find the equation of the axis of symmetry, and the coordinates of the vertex.

(c) Sketch the parabola.

Solution

(a) The coefficient of x^2 is negative, so the graph is n-shaped.

Putting $x = 0$ gives $y = 8$, so the y-intercept is 8.

Putting $y = 0$ gives
$$0 = -x^2 + 2x + 8.$$

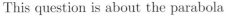 Multiply through by -1 to make factorising easier.

$$0 = x^2 - 2x - 8$$
$$(x + 2)(x - 4) = 0$$
$$x + 2 = 0 \quad \text{or} \quad x - 4 = 0$$
$$x = -2 \quad \text{or} \quad x = 4$$

So the x-intercepts are -2 and 4.

(b) The axis of symmetry is halfway between the x-intercepts.

The number halfway between the x-intercepts is
$$\frac{-2 + 4}{2} = \frac{2}{2} = 1,$$
so the axis of symmetry is the line with equation $x = 1$.

To find the number halfway between two numbers, add them together and divide by 2. In other words, calculate their mean.

The vertex is on the axis of symmetry.

Hence the x-coordinate of the vertex is 1.

Substituting $x = 1$ into the equation of the parabola gives
$$y = -(1)^2 + 2 \times 1 + 8 = -1 + 2 + 8 = 9.$$

So the vertex is $(1, 9)$.

(c) Plot the intercepts and the vertex, and draw the axis of symmetry. Hence sketch the parabola and label it with its equation. Indicate the values of the intercepts and the coordinates of the vertex. 🗨

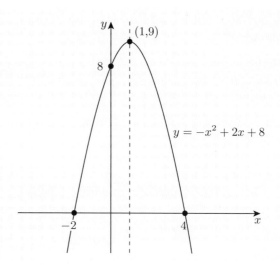

Here is a summary of how to sketch the graph of a quadratic function.

Strategy *To sketch the graph of a quadratic function*

1. Find whether the parabola is u-shaped or n-shaped.

2. Find its intercepts, axis of symmetry and vertex.

3. Plot the features found, and hence sketch the parabola.

4. Label the parabola with its equation, and make sure that the values of the intercepts and the coordinates of the vertex are indicated.

You can practise drawing sketch graphs of quadratic equations in the next two activities. Try to draw each parabola smoothly through the points that you have plotted, and symmetrically on each side of the axis of symmetry. Sometimes finding and plotting one or two extra points on the parabola can help you to draw a good sketch.

As when you draw straight-line graphs, when you sketch parabolas it is usually best to use equal scales on the axes, unless that makes the graph hard to draw or interpret, in which case you should use different scales.

Activity 9 *Sketching the graph of a quadratic function*

Use the strategy above to draw a neat sketch of the graph of the equation $y = x^2 + 5x - 6$.

you have seen, to find the x-intercepts of a parabola you need to solve a dratic equation. If you obtain just one solution, then the graph has just x-intercept. In this case, the single point where the graph touches the is is the vertex, and the vertical line through this point is the axis of symmetry. You can use this information, together with the y-intercept, to sketch the graph in the usual way. Try this in the next activity.

Activity 10   *Sketching the graph of a quadratic function with one x-intercept*

Sketch the graph of the equation $y = 9x^2 - 6x + 1$.

You have seen that you can often find the axis of symmetry of a parabola by using the fact that it lies halfway between the x-intercepts. An alternative method is to use the formula below. This formula can be used when the parabola has no x-intercepts, and you might prefer to use it in other cases too.

A formula for the axis of symmetry of a parabola

The axis of symmetry of the parabola with equation $y = ax^2 + bx + c$ is the line with equation

$$x = -\frac{b}{2a}.$$

For example, to use the formula to work out the axis of symmetry of the parabola $y = -x^2 + 2x + 8$, which was considered in Example 2 on page 145, you substitute $a = -1$ and $b = 2$, which gives

$$x = -\frac{2}{2 \times (-1)}; \quad \text{that is,} \quad x = 1.$$

This is the same line as was found in Example 2.

To see why the formula works, consider the equation

$$y = ax^2 + bx + c,$$

where a, b and c are constants with $a \neq 0$. You know that the graph of this equation is the same as the graph of

$$y = ax^2 + bx,$$

except that it is shifted vertically. So the two graphs have the same axis of symmetry. The x-intercepts of the second graph can be found by factorisation:

$$ax^2 + bx = 0$$
$$x(ax + b) = 0$$
$$x = 0 \quad \text{or} \quad ax + b = 0$$
$$x = 0 \quad \text{or} \quad x = -\frac{b}{a}.$$

The value halfway between 0 and $-\dfrac{b}{a}$ is

$$\frac{1}{2}\left(0 + \left(-\frac{b}{a}\right)\right) = -\frac{b}{2a},$$

so the axis of symmetry is the line $x = -\dfrac{b}{2a}$.

In the next activity you are asked to sketch the graph of a quadratic equation that has no x-intercepts.

Activity 11   *Sketching a quadratic function with no x-intercepts*

Find the y-intercept, axis of symmetry and vertex of the graph of the equation

$$y = x^2 + 2x + 3,$$

and hence sketch the graph.

In this section you have seen that the graph of an equation of the form $y = ax^2 + bx + c$, where a, b and c are constants with $a \neq 0$, is always a u-shaped or n-shaped parabola. The sign of the constant a tells you whether the parabola is u-shaped or n-shaped, and the magnitude of a determines how wide it is. The y-intercept of the graph is c. The position of the vertex depends on the values of all three coefficients, and you will find out more about this later in the unit.

You have also learned how to sketch the graphs of quadratic functions.

3   Solving quadratic equations

In Unit 9 you saw that you can often use factorisation to find the solutions of a quadratic equation. However, sometimes it is not possible to factorise a quadratic expression in the way that you saw in Unit 9, and even if there is such a factorisation, it can be hard to find it.

In this section you will see two more ways to find the solutions of a quadratic equation, which can be used when factorisation is difficult. You will also learn how to tell how many solutions a quadratic equation has, from the values of its coefficients. You will meet yet another way to solve quadratic equations in Section 4.

The section also includes some real-life problems in which solving a quadratic equation is helpful.

3.1   Solving quadratic equations graphically

If you need only *approximate* values for the solutions of a quadratic equation $ax^2 + bx + c = 0$, then one way to find them is to obtain a fairly accurate graph of the corresponding quadratic function $y = ax^2 + bx + c$ and read off the values of x when $y = 0$, that is, the x-intercepts.

For example, consider the quadratic equation

$$x^2 + 3x - 6 = 0. \tag{8}$$

The quadratic expression on the left-hand side cannot be factorised using integers, so the quadratic equation cannot be solved in this way. However, from Figure 27, which shows the graph of the equation $y = x^2 + 3x - 6$, you can see that this equation has two solutions, which are approximately $x = -4.4$ and $x = 1.4$.

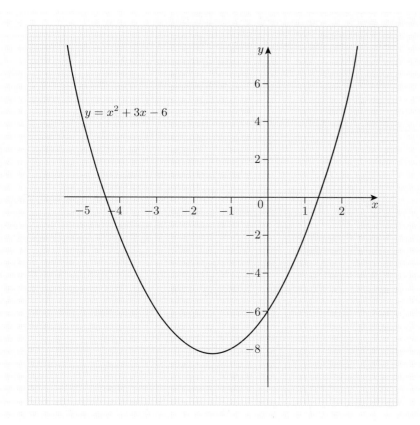

Figure 27 The graph of $y = x^2 + 3x - 6$

If you use Graphplotter to plot the graph of the quadratic function corresponding to a quadratic equation, then you can obtain the solutions more accurately.

For example, suppose that you want to find the solutions of equation (8) to two decimal places. To do this, you plot the graph of the equation $y = x^2 + 3x - 6$ on Graphplotter, and tick the 'Trace' option, which allows you to find the coordinates of points on the graph by moving the cursor.

Then you zoom in on a point where the graph crosses the x-axis, until the x-coordinates of the trace points are given to at least three decimal places (that is, at least one more decimal place than the precision that you eventually want). You can zoom in by clicking repeatedly on the 'Zoom in' button or using the mouse wheel – you will have to drag the graph or use the arrow buttons to keep the crossing point visible in the graph window. Alternatively, you can type appropriate values into the x min, x max, y min and y max boxes, to set the minimum and maximum values of the axis scales.

If you can find two trace points, one below the crossing point and one above, whose x-coordinates are the same when rounded to two decimal places, then the x-intercept must also be the same when rounded to two decimal places.

The next example demonstrates how to use this method to find each solution of equation (8).

Example 3   *Using Graphplotter to find approximate solutions*

Use Graphplotter to find the solutions of the quadratic equation

$$x^2 + 3x - 6 = 0$$

to two decimal places.

Solution

The two screenshots below are obtained by plotting the graph of
$y = x^2 + 3x - 6$ and zooming in on one of the points where the graph
crosses the x-axis. They show that there is a point on the graph below the
x-axis with an x-coordinate of 1.371 to three decimal places, and a point
on the graph above the x-axis with an x-coordinate of 1.374 to three
decimal places. Since both of these values are 1.37 when rounded to two
decimal places, and an x-intercept lies between them, it is also 1.37 to two
decimal places. So one of the solutions of the equation is 1.37 (to 2 d.p.).

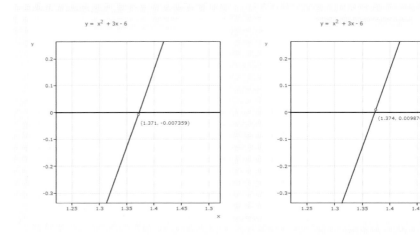

The two screenshots below are obtained by zooming in on the other
crossing point. They show that there is a point on the graph below the
x-axis with an x-coordinate of -4.371 to three decimal places, and a point
on the graph above the x-axis with an x-coordinate of -4.373 to three
decimal places. Since both of these values are -4.37 when rounded to two
decimal places, and an x-intercept lies between them, it is also -4.37 to
two decimal places. So the other solution of the equation is -4.37
(to 2 d.p.).

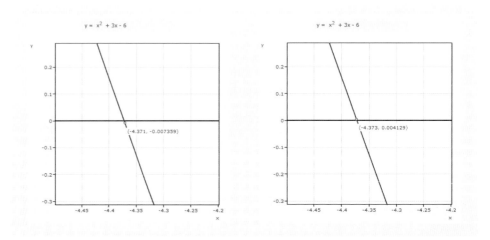

It is easier to use the Trace option on Graphplotter for the method demonstrated in Example 3 if the graph doesn't look too horizontal or too vertical at the crossing point, so sometimes it might be helpful to adjust the scale on the y-axis to achieve this.

Remember also that Graphplotter does not display *trailing zeros*, so, for example, an x-coordinate of 2.70 is displayed as 2.7.

In the next activity you can try the method of Example 3 for yourself.

Activity 12   *Solving a quadratic equation graphically*

Graphplotter

Use Graphplotter, with the 'One graph' tab selected. On the Options page, ensure that 'Trace' is ticked, and 'Coordinates' and 'y-intercept' are not ticked.

(a) Plot the graph of $y = -x^2 + 2x + 7$.

(b) Hence find the solutions of the quadratic equation $-x^2 + 2x + 7 = 0$, to two decimal places.

> If you used Graphplotter to test Example 3 for yourself, then you may have reset the axis scales by zooming in, and so the graph in Activity 12 may not be visible. You can return the axis scales to their default values by pressing 'Autoscale'.

You can use a similar method to find the x-coordinate of any point on a graph, given its y-coordinate. Try this in the next activity.

Activity 13   *Using Graphplotter to find an x-coordinate*

Graphplotter

Use Graphplotter, with the 'One graph' tab selected. On the Options page, ensure that 'Trace' is ticked, and 'Coordinates' and 'y-intercept' are not ticked.

In Subsection 1.1, on page 131, you saw that if a ball is dropped out of a window at a height of 26 m, then its height y metres after it has been dropping for x seconds is given by the equation

$$y = 26 - 4.9x^2.$$

> On page 131 the variables t and h were used instead of x and y, but x and y are used here because they are the variables used by Graphplotter.

Use Graphplotter to find the time taken by the ball to fall to a height of 20 m, to the nearest tenth of a second. To do this, plot the graph of the equation above, and set the x-axis scale to be 0 to 3 and the y-axis scale to be 0 to 30. Then move the cursor left and right to find a point on the graph with a y-coordinate just less than 20 and a point on the graph with a y-coordinate just greater than 20. You should find that you already have the precision that you need in the x-coordinates – there is no need to zoom in.

In Activity 13 you used Graphplotter to find the x-coordinate of a point on a graph, given its y-coordinate. Remember that it is straightforward to go the other way; that is, to find the y-coordinate of a point on a graph, given its x-coordinate. To do this, you first need to make sure that 'Trace' is ticked, then type the x-coordinate into the x-coordinate box, press 'Enter' and look at the coordinates of the trace point.

> This method for finding y-coordinates was given in Activity 2 on page 131.

Graphplotter calculates y-coordinates from x-coordinates, so, for example, if a trace point on a graph is shown with coordinates $(1.87, 12.6052)$, then it means that an x-coordinate of exactly 1.87 gives a y-coordinate of 12.6052 correct to four decimal places. Remember though that

Graphplotter does not display trailing zeros, so, for example, if the x-coordinate 2.07 gives a y-coordinate of 9.1440 to four decimal places, then these coordinates are displayed as $(2.07, 9.144)$.

You saw earlier that the graph of a quadratic function has two, one or zero x-intercepts. Notice that this tells you that every quadratic equation has either two, one or zero solutions.

3.2 The quadratic formula

The first person to give a formula for solving quadratic equations was the Indian mathematician Brahmagupta, in 628. He described the formula in words, but it was essentially the same as the modern quadratic formula.

The **quadratic formula**, given below, provides a systematic way to find the exact solutions of any quadratic equation.

> **The quadratic formula**
>
> The solutions of the quadratic equation
> $$ax^2 + bx + c = 0$$
> are given by
> $$x = \frac{-b \pm \sqrt{b^2 - 4ac}}{2a}.$$

You will see why the formula works later in the unit, but for now you should concentrate on how to use it. Here is an example.

Example 4   *Using the quadratic formula*

Use the quadratic formula to solve the equation $3x^2 - 2x - 5 = 0$.

Solution

💬 Check that the equation is in the form $ax^2 + bx + c = 0$, and find the values of a, b and c. 💬

Here $a = 3$, $b = -2$ and $c = -5$. Substituting into the quadratic formula gives

$$\begin{aligned}
x &= \frac{-b \pm \sqrt{b^2 - 4ac}}{2a} \\
&= \frac{-(-2) \pm \sqrt{(-2)^2 - 4 \times 3 \times (-5)}}{2 \times 3} \\
&= \frac{2 \pm \sqrt{4 + 60}}{6} \\
&= \frac{2 \pm \sqrt{64}}{6} \\
&= \frac{2 \pm 8}{6} \\
&= \frac{2 + 8}{6} \quad \text{or} \quad \frac{2 - 8}{6} \\
&= \frac{10}{6} \quad \text{or} \quad \frac{-6}{6} \\
&= \tfrac{5}{3} \quad \text{or} \quad -1.
\end{aligned}$$

So the solutions are $x = \frac{5}{3}$ and $x = -1$.

The quadratic equation in Example 4 could alternatively have been solved by using factorisation, as shown below:

$$3x^2 - 2x - 5 = 0$$
$$(3x - 5)(x + 1) = 0$$
$$3x - 5 = 0 \quad \text{or} \quad x + 1 = 0$$
$$x = \tfrac{5}{3} \quad \text{or} \quad x = -1.$$

This working is shorter and simpler than the working for the quadratic formula. So it is always worth checking whether a given quadratic equation can be factorised easily before you resort to using the quadratic formula. Factorising is often the quickest way to solve a quadratic equation, and the least likely to lead to mistakes.

The quadratic equation in Example 5 below cannot easily be factorised. In fact, its solutions turn out to be irrational, which confirms that it cannot be factorised using any rational numbers.

Example 5 *Using the quadratic formula again*

Tutorial clip

Use the quadratic formula to solve the equation $2x^2 + 4x - 7 = 0$.

Solution

Here $a = 2$, $b = 4$ and $c = -7$. Substituting into the quadratic formula gives

$$
\begin{aligned}
x &= \frac{-b \pm \sqrt{b^2 - 4ac}}{2a} \\
&= \frac{-4 \pm \sqrt{4^2 - 4 \times 2 \times (-7)}}{2 \times 2} \\
&= \frac{-4 \pm \sqrt{16 + 56}}{4} \\
&= \frac{-4 \pm \sqrt{72}}{4} \\
&= \frac{-4 \pm 6\sqrt{2}}{4} \\
&= -1 \pm \tfrac{3}{2}\sqrt{2}.
\end{aligned}
$$

Note that
$$\sqrt{72} = \sqrt{36 \times 2} = 6\sqrt{2}.$$

So the solutions are

$$x = -1 + \tfrac{3}{2}\sqrt{2} \quad \text{and} \quad x = -1 - \tfrac{3}{2}\sqrt{2}.$$

The answers to Example 5 were left in surd form, so that they are exact. If they had been the answers to a problem in a real-life context, or were to be used to plot points on a graph, then it would be more sensible to give them as decimal approximations.

Notice also that the surds in Example 5 are expressed in their simplest form, by writing $\sqrt{72}$ as $6\sqrt{2}$. If you give the solutions to a quadratic equation as surds, then you should write them in their simplest form, using the methods that you learned in Unit 3. Sometimes you might find it helpful to use your calculator – the calculator recommended for the module can simplify surds.

Notice that in the last line of the working in Example 5, the expression

$$\frac{-4 \pm 6\sqrt{2}}{4} \tag{9}$$

was expanded to give

$$-1 \pm \tfrac{3}{2}\sqrt{2}.$$

An alternative way to simplify expression (9) is to cancel the common factor 2 in the numerator and denominator, to give

$$x = \frac{-2 \pm 3\sqrt{2}}{2},$$

and then state the solutions as

$$x = \frac{-2 + 3\sqrt{2}}{2} \quad \text{and} \quad x = \frac{-2 - 3\sqrt{2}}{2}.$$

Either of these ways of writing the solutions is just as simple, and just as acceptable, as the other.

You can practise using the quadratic formula in the next activity.

Activity 14   *Using the quadratic formula*

Use the quadratic formula to solve the following quadratic equations.

(a) $x^2 + 6x + 1 = 0$ (b) $3x^2 - 8x - 2 = 0$

Remember to check that your quadratic equation is in the form $ax^2 + bx + c = 0$ before you apply the quadratic formula! If it is not in this form, then you must rearrange it before you identify the values of a, b and c. For example, if you want to solve the equation

$$3x^2 + 2x = 4,$$

then you should first rearrange it as

$$3x^2 + 2x - 4 = 0,$$

which gives $a = 3$, $b = 2$ and $c = -4$.

Another thing to think about before you start to solve a quadratic equation is whether it is in its simplest form. You saw the following suggestions in Unit 9.

> **Simplifying a quadratic equation**
>
> - If the coefficient of x^2 is negative, then multiply the equation through by -1 to make this coefficient positive.
>
> - If the coefficients have a common factor, then divide the equation through by this factor.
>
> - If any of the coefficients are fractions, then multiply the equation through by a suitable number to clear them.

For example, you can simplify the quadratic equation

$$-2x^2 - 2x + 6 = 0$$

by multiplying through by -1 (to make the coefficient of x^2 positive) and dividing through by 2 (to make all the coefficients smaller). This gives

$$x^2 + x - 3 = 0,$$

which you can then proceed to solve.

Activity 15 *Rearranging and solving a quadratic equation*

Clear the fraction in the quadratic equation

$$-x^2 = -x - \tfrac{3}{2}$$

and use the quadratic formula to solve it.

Now that you have a way of solving quadratic equations that you could not solve by factorising, you can solve many more problems involving quadratic functions. Here is one for you to try.

Activity 16 *The picture framer's problem*

A picture framer always mounts photographs on a white rectangular backboard that has an area 50% larger than the area of the photograph, and whose dimensions are such that the white border around the photograph is the same width all the way round. The diagram below shows a mounted 12 inch by 18 inch photograph, with the width of the white border labelled as x. All the labelled lengths are in inches.

Standard photograph sizes in the UK are usually given in inches rather than centimetres. An inch is about 2.54 cm.

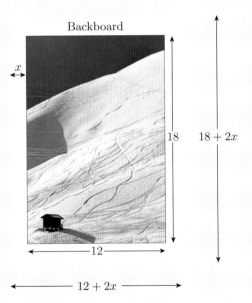

In this question you are asked to find the dimensions of the backboard, as follows.

(a) Explain in words why the width and height of the backboard, in inches, are $12 + 2x$ and $18 + 2x$, respectively.

(b) Use the fact that the area of the backboard is 50% larger than the area of the photograph to find the area of the backboard, in square inches.

(c) Find an algebraic expression for the area of the backboard in terms of x.

(d) Use your answers to parts (b) and (c) to show that $x^2 + 15x - 27 = 0$.

(e) Solve the quadratic equation in part (d), and hence find the width of the white border and the dimensions of the backboard to the nearest tenth of an inch.

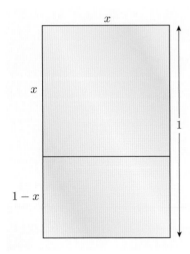

Figure 28 The golden rectangle

There is a story that the ancient Greeks believed that the most aesthetically pleasing shape of rectangle was the shape such that if you cut it into a square and a smaller rectangle, as shown in Figure 28, then the smaller rectangle has the same shape – that is, the same aspect ratio – as the original rectangle. This shape is known as the *golden rectangle*.

You can work out the aspect ratio of the golden rectangle as follows. If the length and width of the larger rectangle are 1 and x, respectively (in any units), then the larger and smaller rectangles have aspect ratios $1 : x$ and $x : (1 - x)$, respectively, as you can see from Figure 28. Since these two aspect ratios are equivalent, and the first aspect ratio is equivalent to $x : x^2$, the number x must satisfy the equation $x^2 = 1 - x$. You can use the quadratic formula to find the solutions of this equation. The solutions are $\frac{1}{2}(-1 \pm \sqrt{5})$, only one of which, $\frac{1}{2}(-1 + \sqrt{5})$, is positive. So the aspect ratio of the golden rectangle is $1 : \frac{1}{2}(-1 + \sqrt{5})$, and this ratio is known as the *golden ratio*.

Finally in this subsection, it is worth noticing how the quadratic formula relates to the equation of the axis of symmetry of a parabola. The quadratic formula can be rearranged slightly as

$$x = -\frac{b}{2a} \pm \frac{\sqrt{b^2 - 4ac}}{2a}.$$

You can see from this form of the formula that the value of x halfway between the two solutions of the quadratic equation $ax^2 + bx + c = 0$ is $x = -b/(2a)$. This is the equation that you saw on page 147 for the axis of symmetry of the parabola with equation $y = ax^2 + bx + c$, as you would expect.

3.3 The number of solutions of a quadratic equation

You have seen that some quadratic equations have no solutions – this occurs when the corresponding graph has no x-intercepts. If you try to use the quadratic formula to solve such a quadratic equation, then the fact that there are no solutions quickly becomes clear. For example, consider the equation

$$x^2 + 7x + 13 = 0.$$

Here $a = 1$, $b = 7$ and $c = 13$, and substituting these values into the quadratic formula gives

$$\begin{aligned}
x &= \frac{-b \pm \sqrt{b^2 - 4ac}}{2a} = \frac{-7 \pm \sqrt{7^2 - 4 \times 1 \times 13}}{2 \times 1} \\
&= \frac{-7 \pm \sqrt{49 - 52}}{2} \\
&= \frac{-7 \pm \sqrt{-3}}{2}.
\end{aligned}$$

This expression involves the number $\sqrt{-3}$, but there is no such number, because negative numbers do not have square roots. So the equation has no solutions. This is confirmed by the graph in Figure 29.

From this example you can see that it is the value of the expression $b^2 - 4ac$, which appears under the square root sign in the quadratic formula, that determines whether a quadratic equation has any solutions. In general, if $b^2 - 4ac$ is negative, then there are no solutions.

The value of $b^2 - 4ac$ also determines whether a quadratic equation has two solutions or just one. For example, consider the equation

$$4x^2 - 12x + 9 = 0.$$

Here $a = 4$, $b = -12$ and $c = 9$, and substituting these values into the quadratic formula gives

$$
\begin{aligned}
x &= \frac{-b \pm \sqrt{b^2 - 4ac}}{2a} \\
&= \frac{-(-12) \pm \sqrt{(-12)^2 - 4 \times 4 \times 9}}{2 \times 4} \\
&= \frac{12 \pm \sqrt{144 - 144}}{8} \\
&= \frac{12 \pm \sqrt{0}}{8} \\
&= \frac{3}{2}.
\end{aligned}
$$

So this equation has only one solution. This is confirmed by the graph in Figure 30.

You can see that, in general, if $b^2 - 4ac$ is zero, then there is only one solution.

The value $b^2 - 4ac$ is called the **discriminant** of the quadratic expression $ax^2 + bx + c$.

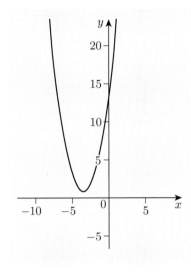

Figure 29 The graph of $y = x^2 + 7x + 13$

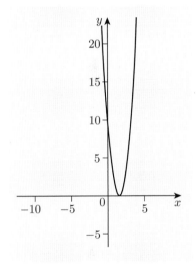

Figure 30 The graph of $y = 4x^2 - 12x + 9$

The number of solutions of a quadratic equation

The quadratic equation $ax^2 + bx + c = 0$ has:

- two solutions if $b^2 - 4ac > 0$ (the discriminant is positive)
- one solution if $b^2 - 4ac = 0$ (the discriminant is zero)
- no solutions if $b^2 - 4ac < 0$ (the discriminant is negative).

Activity 17 *Predicting the number of solutions of a quadratic equation*

Use the discriminant to determine whether each of the following quadratic equations has two, one or no solutions. Find any solutions.

(a) $9x^2 + 30x + 25 = 0$ (b) $x^2 - 4x - 2 = 0$ (c) $-3x^2 + 5x = 4$

Although some quadratic equations have no solutions among the real numbers, all quadratic equations have either one or two solutions among the *complex numbers*, which were mentioned in Unit 3. The complex numbers consist of all the usual real numbers, together with many 'imaginary' numbers, including the square roots of negative numbers. Finding the imaginary solutions of a quadratic equation can be more useful than you might think! For example, they are used in many engineering mathematical models, such as those used to design car suspensions. You can learn about the imaginary solutions of quadratic equations if you go on to study more mathematics.

3.4 Vertically-launched projectiles

Imagine dropping a ball from the top of a cliff of height $12\,\text{m}$. From Section 1, you know that after t seconds the ball will have fallen $\frac{1}{2}gt^2$ metres, where g is the acceleration due to gravity (about $9.8\,\text{m/s}^2$). So its height h metres above the ground below the cliff after t seconds is given by the equation

$$h = 12 - \tfrac{1}{2}gt^2.$$

Now imagine throwing the ball vertically up from the top edge of the cliff, with an initial speed of $2.8\,\text{m/s}$, instead of just dropping it. There are two factors influencing the motion of the ball – gravity and its initial speed. You can find a formula for the height of the ball after t seconds by considering the effects of both factors separately, and adding them together.

If there were no gravity (or any other forces acting on the ball), and you threw the ball upwards with a speed of $2.8\,\text{m/s}$, then it would continue to move at that constant speed, and so after t seconds its height would have increased by $2.8t$ metres.

On the other hand, if the ball had no initial speed, but just moved under the effect of gravity, then after t seconds its height would have decreased by $\frac{1}{2}gt^2$ metres.

Putting these two facts together, and using the fact that the initial height of the ball is $12\,\text{m}$, gives the following formula for the height h metres of the ball after t seconds:

$$h = 12 + 2.8t - \tfrac{1}{2}gt^2.$$

Writing the terms on the right-hand side in their usual order (with the term in t^2 first and the constant term last), and using the fact that $g = 9.8$, gives

$$h = -4.9t^2 + 2.8t + 12.$$

Figure 31 shows the graph of this equation. You can see that, as you would expect, the ball initially rises, and then starts to fall. It reaches the ground below the cliff in a little less than 2 seconds.

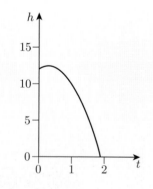

Figure 31   The graph of $h = -4.9t^2 + 2.8t + 12$

You can use the quadratic formula to find a more accurate estimate for the time that the ball takes to reach the ground. This is given by the value of t for which $h = 0$, so you need to solve the quadratic equation

$$-4.9t^2 + 2.8t + 12 = 0.$$

Before using the quadratic formula, let's multiply through by -1 to make the coefficient of t^2 positive. This is not essential, but it makes the numbers slightly easier to work with. This gives

$$4.9t^2 - 2.8t - 12 = 0.$$

Here $a = 4.9$, $b = -2.8$ and $c = -12$, and substituting these numbers into the quadratic formula gives

$$
\begin{aligned}
t &= \frac{-b \pm \sqrt{b^2 - 4ac}}{2a} \\
&= \frac{-(-2.8) \pm \sqrt{(-2.8)^2 - 4 \times 4.9 \times (-12)}}{2 \times 4.9} \\
&= \frac{2.8 \pm \sqrt{7.84 + 235.2}}{9.8} \\
&= \frac{2.8 \pm \sqrt{243.04}}{9.8}.
\end{aligned}
$$

Using a calculator gives

$$t = -1.3 \quad \text{or} \quad t = 1.9 \quad \text{(to 1 d.p.).}$$

The negative solution does not make sense in this context, so we disregard it. So the ball reaches the ground below the cliff after approximately 1.9 seconds.

In general, suppose that an object is launched upwards from an initial height h_0 metres with an initial speed v_0 metres per second. Then after t seconds, the increase in height due to the initial speed is $v_0 t$ metres, and the decrease in height due to gravity is $\frac{1}{2}gt^2$ metres. This gives the general formula below.

> Think of h_0 and v_0 as single symbols; they represent constants. They are pronounced as *h-nought* and *v-nought*, respectively. The significance of the zeros is that the symbols denote the height and speed of the object at time $t = 0$. The symbol v is often used for speed, as it is the first letter of 'velocity'.

The motion of a vertically-launched projectile

If an object is launched upwards from an initial height h_0 with an initial speed v_0, then after time t its height h is given by

$$h = -\tfrac{1}{2}gt^2 + v_0 t + h_0, \tag{10}$$

where g is the acceleration due to gravity, which is about $9.8\,\text{m/s}^2$.

Of course, as with all the formulas for falling objects in this unit, this formula is only a model, and in real life the motion of an object will differ to some extent from that predicted by the formula, largely due to air resistance.

Try using this formula in the activity below.

Activity 18 *Finding the descent time of a toy rocket*

The fuel in a toy rocket runs out at a height of 155 m above the ground, at which point it has an upwards speed of 49 m/s. After how many seconds does the toy rocket return to the ground? Give your answer to one decimal place.

Formula (10) in the box above can be used to predict the motion of a projectile launched at an angle, such as a cannonball fired at an angle of $45°$ to the ground, as shown in Figure 17 on page 136. This is done by considering the horizontal and vertical motion of the projectile separately, in the way that you saw in Section 1. Formula (10) models the vertical motion, and the horizontal motion is modelled by the usual distance–speed–time formula for constant speed, as before. Before these formulas can be applied, it is necessary to calculate how much of the initial speed contributes to vertical motion and how much contributes to horizontal motion. You can find out how to do this in higher-level mathematics modules – it involves trigonometry, which you will learn about in Unit 12.

As mentioned in Section 1, the trajectory of such a projectile is always parabolic, which is why, for example, the shape of a jet of water in a fountain is a parabola. Figure 32 shows the parabolic trajectories of a bouncing ball.

In this section you have learned two new ways to solve quadratic equations: by using a graph, which gives approximate solutions, and by using the quadratic formula, which gives exact solutions. You have applied these methods to some practical problems.

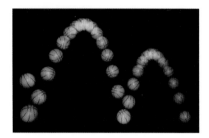

Figure 32   The parabolas formed by the trajectories of a bouncing ball

4 Completing the square

In this section you will learn a useful way of rearranging a quadratic expression, which is called *completing the square*. This method allows you to understand why the graph of any quadratic function is the same shape as the graph of an equation of the form $y = ax^2$, but shifted horizontally or vertically or both.

The method also gives you an alternative way to find the vertex of a parabola, and an alternative way to solve a quadratic equation. Once you have learned the method, it can be a quick way of doing these things.

Completing the square is also the idea behind the quadratic formula – it is why the quadratic formula works, as you will see.

4.1   Shifting parabolas

We begin by looking at what happens when you start with a parabola of the form $y = ax^2$ and shift it relative to the axes.

Figure 33 shows the graph of the equation $y = 2x^2$. As you know, its vertex is the origin. A second parabola has been drawn on the same axes – this parabola is exactly the same shape as the first parabola, but it is shifted three units to the right and one unit up.

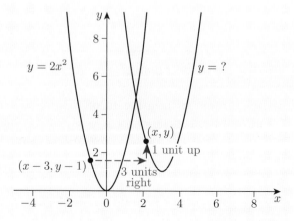

Figure 33   The graph of $y = 2x^2$ and the graph obtained by shifting it 3 units to the right and 1 unit up

Let's consider whether we can use the equation of the first parabola to work out an equation for the second. Let (x, y) be any point on the *second* parabola. Then (x, y) is the result of shifting a corresponding point on the first parabola, as shown in the diagram. This corresponding point is 3 units left and 1 unit down from (x, y), so its coordinates are

$$(x - 3, y - 1).$$

Because *this* point lies on the first parabola, *its* coordinates satisfy the equation

$$\left(y\text{-coordinate} \right) = 2 \times \left(x\text{-coordinate} \right)^2.$$

So

$$y - 1 = 2(x - 3)^2.$$

Since x and y refer to the second parabola, this is an equation that is satisfied by every point (x, y) on the second parabola, so it is the equation of the second parabola. It can be rearranged to get y by itself on the left-hand side, as follows:

$$y = 2(x - 3)^2 + 1.$$

The equation can be left in this form, or it can be multiplied out to give the more usual form:

$$\begin{aligned} y &= 2(x^2 - 6x + 9) + 1 \\ &= 2x^2 - 12x + 18 + 1 \\ &= 2x^2 - 12x + 19. \end{aligned}$$

In general, suppose that the parabola with equation $y = ax^2$ is shifted right by h units and up by k units. The numbers h and k can be positive, negative or zero, so the actual shift could be to the right or left, or neither, and up or down, or neither. Then each point (x, y) on the second parabola is a shift of the point $(x - h, y - k)$ on the first parabola, as illustrated in Figure 34.

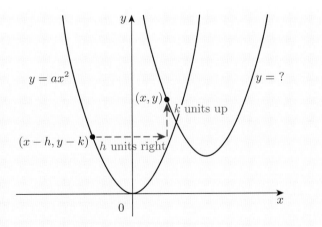

Figure 34 The graph of $y = ax^2$ and the graph obtained by shifting it h units right and k units up

By the same argument as before, we have

$$y - k = a(x - h)^2,$$

or equivalently,

$$y = a(x - h)^2 + k, \tag{11}$$

and this is the equation of the second parabola.

Any equation of form (11) can be multiplied out to give the usual form of the equation of a parabola, $y = ax^2 + bx + c$.

However, the really crucial fact is that you can always go in the other direction, too. That is, *any* equation of the form $y = ax^2 + bx + c$, where a, b and c are constants with $a \neq 0$, can be rearranged into form (11) (where the constants h and k can be positive, negative or zero). You'll learn how to do this in this section.

The fact that the equation of *every* quadratic function is equivalent to an equation of form (11) explains why the graph of every quadratic function is a shift of a parabola of the form $y = ax^2$. You saw that this *seemed* to be the case when you used Graphplotter to investigate the shapes of parabolas in Section 2.

Since h and k can be positive, negative or zero, the fact stated above can be restated as below.

Completed-square form

Every expression of the form $ax^2 + bx + c$, where $a \neq 0$, can be rearranged into the form

$$a\left(x + \boxed{\text{a number}}\right)^2 + \boxed{\text{a number}},$$

where each of the two numbers in this expression can be positive, negative or zero.

This is called the **completed-square form**.

The process of finding the completed-square form of a quadratic expression is called **completing the square**.

It was mentioned earlier that one reason for completing the square is that it gives you a quick way to find the vertex of a parabola. To see how to do this, suppose that you have rearranged the equation of a parabola into the form of equation (11); that is,

$$y = a(x - h)^2 + k.$$

This tells you that the parabola has the same shape as the parabola with equation $y = ax^2$, but shifted h units to the right and k units up, as shown in Figure 34 on the previous page. Since the vertex of the parabola with equation $y = ax^2$ is $(0, 0)$, the vertex of the shifted parabola is (h, k).

This useful result is summarised below.

The parabola with equation

$$y = a(x - h)^2 + k$$

has vertex (h, k).

For example, suppose that you have rearranged the equation of a parabola into the completed-square form

$$y = 3(x + 5)^2 + 8.$$

Here $h = -5$ and $k = 8$, so the vertex is $(-5, 8)$.

It can be difficult to remember exactly how to obtain the coordinates of the vertex from the completed-square form. One way to remember it is to use the fact that the vertex always corresponds to the minimum or maximum value of y (depending on whether the parabola is u-shaped or n-shaped). For example, consider again the completed-square form

$$y = 3(x + 5)^2 + 8.$$

The parabola that is the graph of this equation is u-shaped, because when you multiply out the brackets, the coefficient of x^2 will be 3, which is positive. So the vertex of this parabola corresponds to the *minimum* value of y.

Notice that the equation contains the expression $(x + 5)^2$, and the minimum value of this expression is 0, because the square of a number is never negative. So the minimum value of $3(x + 5)^2$ is also 0, and hence the minimum value of the whole expression $3(x + 5)^2 + 8$ is 8. That is, the y-coordinate of the vertex is 8.

This minimum value occurs when the expression that is squared is zero, that is, when $x + 5 = 0$ or $x = -5$. So the x-coordinate of the vertex is -5, and hence the vertex is $(-5, 8)$, as found above.

Here is another example of finding the vertex from a completed-square form in this way.

Example 6   *Finding the vertex of a parabola from its completed-square form*

State whether the parabola with equation

$$y = -(x - 2)^2 - 3$$

is u-shaped or n-shaped, and write down the coordinates of its vertex.

Solution

The parabola is n-shaped, because the coefficient of x^2 is -1, which is negative.

The minimum value of $(x - 2)^2$ is 0, so the *maximum* value of $-(x - 2)^2$ is 0, and hence the maximum value of $-(x - 2)^2 - 3$ is -3.

This occurs when $x - 2 = 0$, that is, when $x = 2$.

The vertex is $(2, -3)$.

Here are some similar examples for you to try.

Activity 19   *Finding the vertices of parabolas from completed-square forms*

For each of the following equations, state whether the parabola is u-shaped or n-shaped, and write down the coordinates of its vertex.

(a) $y = (x + 1)^2 + 5$ (b) $y = -2(x + 3)^2 + 7$ (c) $y = 7(x - 1)^2 - 4$

(d) $y = -\left(x + \frac{1}{2}\right)^2 - 1$ (e) $y = x^2 + 3$ (f) $y = (x - 2)^2$

In the next subsection you will learn the basic method for completing the square in a quadratic expression.

4.2 Completing the square in quadratics of the form $x^2 + bx + c$

In this subsection you will learn how to complete the square in quadratic expressions in which the coefficient of x^2 is 1. Other quadratics are covered in Subsection 4.4.

The completed-square form of a quadratic in which the coefficient of x^2 is 1 is

$$\left(x + \boxed{\text{a number}} \right)^2 + \boxed{\text{a number}} .$$

This is the expression given in the first pink box on page 162, with $a = 1$.

We begin by looking at completing the square in quadratics in which not only does x^2 have coefficient 1, but the constant term is zero – that is, expressions such as $x^2 + 8x$, $x^2 + 10x$ or $x^2 - 6x$. In other words, we will look at quadratics of the form $x^2 + bx$.

Completing the square in quadratics of the form $x^2 + bx$

You saw how to expand squared brackets in Unit 9.

To see how to complete the square in a quadratic expression of this form, first consider the following examples of expanding squared brackets.

$$(x + 1)^2 = x^2 + 2x + 1$$
$$(x - 2)^2 = x^2 - 4x + 4$$
$$(x + 3)^2 = x^2 + 6x + 9$$

In general, for any number p, positive, negative or zero,

$$(x + p)^2 = x^2 + 2px + p^2.$$

The expression on the right-hand side of each equation above is of the form $x^2 + bx$ plus an extra number. If you subtract this extra number from both sides of each equation, and swap the sides, then you obtain

$$x^2 + 2x = (x + 1)^2 - 1,$$
$$x^2 - 4x = (x - 2)^2 - 4,$$
$$x^2 + 6x = (x + 3)^2 - 9,$$

and in general,

$$x^2 + 2px = (x + p)^2 - p^2.$$

The expressions on the right-hand sides of the equations above are in completed-square form, so they are the completed-square forms of the expressions on the left. In each case the constant term in the brackets on the right-hand side is half of the coefficient of the term in x on the left. For example:

$$x^2 \boxed{+ 6}x = (x \boxed{+ 3})^2 - 9$$

Half of the
coefficient of x

Also, in each case the number that is subtracted on the right-hand side is the square of the constant term in the brackets.

For example:

$$x^2 + 6x = (x + 3)^2 - 9$$

The square of
the number
in brackets

You can see why this is by considering the general case:

$$x^2 + 2px = (x + p)^2 - p^2$$

Half of the   The square of
coefficient of x the number
                     in brackets

You can now see how to write down the completed-square form of any quadratic expression of the form $x^2 + bx$. First you write down $(x \underline{\quad})^2$, filling the gap with the number that is half of b, the coefficient of x. This ensures that you have a squared bracket that, when expanded, gives the terms $x^2 + bx$. However, it also gives an extra term, which is the square of the number in the gap. So you need to subtract this term to obtain a final completed-square form that is equivalent to $x^2 + bx$.

Here is an example.

Example 7   *Completing the square in a quadratic of the form $x^2 + bx$*

Write the quadratic expression $x^2 - 10x$ in completed-square form.

Solution

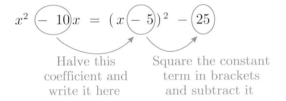

$$x^2 - 10x = (x - 5)^2 - 25$$

Halve this   Square the constant
coefficient and   term in brackets
write it here   and subtract it

You can use the general equation
$$x^2 + 2px = (x + p)^2 - p^2$$
as a 'formula for completing the square', if you prefer to think of the method this way.

Once you have found a completed-square form, you can check that it is correct by multiplying it out. For example, multiplying out the expression on the right-hand side of the equation in the solution to Example 7 gives

$$(x - 5)^2 - 25 = x^2 - 10x + 25 - 25$$
$$= x^2 - 10x,$$

which is the same as the left-hand side, as expected.

Here are some examples of completing the square for you to try.

Activity 20   *Completing the square in quadratics of the form $x^2 + bx$*

Write the following quadratic expressions in completed-square form, and check your answers by multiplying out.

(a) $x^2 + 16x$ (b) $x^2 - 12x$ (c) $t^2 - 2t$ (d) $x^2 + 3x$

Completing the square in quadratics of the form $x^2 + bx + c$

To complete the square in a quadratic of the form $x^2 + bx + c$ whose constant term c is not zero, you just concentrate on the terms in x^2 and x, and complete the square for these terms in the same way as before. Then you have to collect the constant terms. This is illustrated in the example below.

Tutorial clip

Example 8 *Completing the square in quadratics of the form* $x^2 + bx + c$

Write the following quadratic expressions in completed-square form.

(a) $x^2 + 8x + 10$ (b) $x^2 - 3x + 5$

Solution

(a) First complete the square for the sub-expression $x^2 + 8x$, leaving the $+ 10$ unchanged.

$$x^2 + 8x + 10 = (x + 4)^2 - 16 + 10$$

Then collect the constant terms.

$$= (x + 4)^2 - 6$$

(Check:

$$(x + 4)^2 - 6 = x^2 + 8x + 16 - 6$$
$$= x^2 + 8x + 10.)$$

(b) First complete the square for the sub-expression $x^2 - 3x$.

$$x^2 - 3x + 5 = \left(x - \tfrac{3}{2}\right)^2 - \tfrac{9}{4} + 5$$

Then collect the constant terms.

$$= \left(x - \tfrac{3}{2}\right)^2 - \tfrac{9}{4} + \tfrac{20}{4}$$
$$= \left(x - \tfrac{3}{2}\right)^2 + \tfrac{11}{4}.$$

(Check:

$$\left(x - \tfrac{3}{2}\right)^2 + \tfrac{11}{4} = x^2 - 3x + \tfrac{9}{4} + \tfrac{11}{4}$$
$$= x^2 - 3x + 5.)$$

Activity 21 *Completing the square in quadratics of the form* $x^2 + bx + c$

Write the following quadratic expressions in completed-square form, and check your answers by multiplying out.

(a) $x^2 + 6x - 3$ (b) $x^2 - 4x + 9$ (c) $p^2 - 12p - 5$

(d) $x^2 + x + 1$

Here is a summary of the method that you have seen in this subsection.

> **Strategy** *To complete the square in a quadratic of the form* $x^2 + bx + c$
>
> 1. Rewrite the expression with the $x^2 + bx$ part changed to
> $$(x + p)^2 - p^2,$$
>   where the number p is half of b.
> 2. Collect the constant terms.

Remember that in this strategy the number b, and hence the number p, can be either positive or negative. (If b is zero, then the quadratic is already in completed-square form.)

Later in the section you will see how to complete the square in quadratics in which the coefficient of x^2 is not 1. Before that, the next subsection tells you how to solve a quadratic equation by completing the square.

4.3 Solving quadratic equations by completing the square

As mentioned earlier, completing the square gives you another method of solving quadratic equations (and hence of finding the x-intercepts of parabolas).

To solve a quadratic equation in this way, you only ever need to complete the square in expressions of the form $x^2 + bx + c$, that is, in quadratics whose term in x^2 has coefficient 1. This is because you can always divide a quadratic equation through by the coefficient of x^2 to give a quadratic equation whose term in x^2 has coefficient 1. For example, if the quadratic equation is

$$5x^2 - 3x + 10 = 0,$$

then you can divide through by 5 to give

$$x^2 - \tfrac{3}{5}x + 2 = 0.$$

Dividing through by the coefficient of x^2 can turn some of the coefficients in the equation from whole numbers into fractions, but that doesn't matter, as fractions are treated in the same way as any other number when completing the square.

Once you have completed the square in the equation, you can solve the equation as follows. First rearrange it so that the square term and the constant term are on different sides, then take the square root of both sides and finally rearrange the equation again to obtain x by itself on one side. This is illustrated in the example below.

Example 9   *Solving a quadratic equation by completing the square*

Solve the quadratic equation $4x^2 + 8x - 1 = 0$.

Solution

$$4x^2 + 8x - 1 = 0$$

💬 Divide through by the coefficient of x^2. 💬

$$x^2 + 2x - \tfrac{1}{4} = 0$$

The Babylonians in about 1850–1650 BC were able to solve problems equivalent to quadratic equations. Their method was essentially one of completing the square, but they found only positive solutions, as their problems involved positive quantities such as length.

Complete the square.

$$(x+1)^2 - 1 - \tfrac{1}{4} = 0$$
$$(x+1)^2 - \tfrac{5}{4} = 0$$

Get the constant term on the right.

$$(x+1)^2 = \tfrac{5}{4}$$

Take the square root of both sides.

$$x + 1 = \pm\sqrt{\tfrac{5}{4}}$$
$$x + 1 = \pm\tfrac{1}{2}\sqrt{5}$$

Finally, get x by itself on the left.

You could write $x = \pm\tfrac{1}{2}\sqrt{5} - 1$ at this stage, but in an expression like this it is traditional to put the root last.

$$x = -1 \pm \tfrac{1}{2}\sqrt{5}$$

The solutions are $x = -1 + \tfrac{1}{2}\sqrt{5}$ and $x = -1 - \tfrac{1}{2}\sqrt{5}$.

Activity 22   Solving quadratic equations by completing the square

Solve the following quadratic equations by completing the square.

(a) $x^2 + 6x - 5 = 0$ (b) $2x^2 - 12x - 5 = 0$

The derivation of the quadratic formula

You can use the technique of completing the square to rearrange the general quadratic equation

$$ax^2 + bx + c = 0,$$

to obtain x by itself on the left-hand side. The method is the same as in Example 9, but a, b and c are not replaced by particular numbers – they just stay as they are throughout the manipulation. When you do this rearrangement, you end up with the quadratic formula.

The manipulation is given below – read it through if you would like to know why the quadratic formula works.

The equation is

$$ax^2 + bx + c = 0,$$

where $a \neq 0$.

The first step is to divide through by the coefficient of x^2:

$$x^2 + \frac{b}{a}x + \frac{c}{a} = 0.$$

Then you complete the square:

$$\left(x + \frac{b}{2a}\right)^2 - \left(\frac{b}{2a}\right)^2 + \frac{c}{a} = 0$$

$$\left(x + \frac{b}{2a}\right)^2 - \frac{b^2}{4a^2} + \frac{c}{a} = 0.$$

Next you get the constant terms on the right, and combine them into a single fraction:

$$\left(x + \frac{b}{2a}\right)^2 = \frac{b^2}{4a^2} - \frac{c}{a}$$

$$= \frac{b^2}{4a^2} - \frac{4ac}{4a^2}$$

$$= \frac{b^2 - 4ac}{4a^2}.$$

Now you can take the square root of both sides:

$$x + \frac{b}{2a} = \pm\sqrt{\frac{b^2 - 4ac}{4a^2}}$$

$$= \pm\frac{\sqrt{b^2 - 4ac}}{2a}.$$

The last step is to get x by itself on the left-hand side:

$$x = -\frac{b}{2a} \pm \frac{\sqrt{b^2 - 4ac}}{2a}$$

$$= \frac{-b \pm \sqrt{b^2 - 4ac}}{2a}$$

This is the quadratic formula!

4.4 Completing the square in quadratics of the form $ax^2 + bx + c$

So far you have seen how to complete the square in quadratic expressions in which the coefficient of x^2 is 1. In this subsection you will see how to complete the square in quadratic expressions in which the coefficient of x^2 is *not* 1. Although this is not needed to solve quadratic equations, it is useful for finding the vertices of parabolas.

When you are faced with a problem that is different from those that you have seen before, a useful strategy is to try to change it into a form that you recognise. If you have to complete the square in a quadratic expression in which the coefficient of x^2 is not 1, then you can turn this problem into a problem of completing the square when the coefficient *is* 1, by taking the coefficient of x^2 out as a factor. You don't need to take the factor out of all the terms, but just the terms in x^2 and x. For example, to complete the square in the quadratic expression

$$2x^2 + 8x - 7,$$

you can take the common factor 2 out of the first two terms to obtain

$$2(x^2 + 4x) - 7.$$

Then you can complete the square in the quadratic *inside the brackets* in the way that you have seen. To obtain the final completed-square form for the whole expression you just need to simplify the results.

You can take the coefficient of x^2 out of the terms in x^2 and x in a quadratic expression even if it isn't a *common* factor of these terms. You'll see this shortly, but first the example below illustrates the method when the coefficient is a common factor.

Tutorial clip

Example 10 *Completing the square in quadratics of the form*
$ax^2 + bx + c$

Write the following quadratic expressions in completed-square form.

(a) $2x^2 + 8x - 7$ (b) $-x^2 + 8x - 7$

Solution

(a) Concentrate on the sub-expression $2x^2 + 8x$. First take the coefficient of x^2 out of the sub-expression as a common factor.

$$2x^2 + 8x - 7 = 2\left(x^2 + 4x\right) - 7$$

Now the brackets contain a quadratic in which the coefficient of x^2 is 1. Complete the square in it in the usual way, keeping it enclosed within its brackets.

$$= 2\left((x + 2)^2 - 4\right) - 7$$

Multiply out the *outer* brackets. Don't multiply out the inner brackets, because you want the square $(x + 2)^2$ to appear in the final expression.

$$= 2(x + 2)^2 - 8 - 7$$

Collect the constant terms.

$$= 2(x + 2)^2 - 15$$

(Check:

$$2(x + 2)^2 - 15 = 2(x^2 + 4x + 4) - 15$$
$$= 2x^2 + 8x + 8 - 15$$
$$= 2x^2 + 8x - 7.)$$

(b) Concentrate on the sub-expression $-x^2 + 8x$. First take the minus sign out of the sub-expression.

$$-x^2 + 8x - 7 = -(x^2 - 8x) - 7$$

Complete the square in the quadratic inside the brackets.

$$= -\left((x - 4)^2 - 16\right) - 7$$

Multiply out the *outer* brackets.

$$= -(x - 4)^2 + 16 - 7$$

Collect the constant terms.

$$= -(x - 4)^2 + 9$$

(Check:

$$-(x - 4)^2 + 9 = -(x^2 - 8x + 16) + 9$$
$$= -x^2 + 8x - 16 + 9$$
$$= -x^2 + 8x - 7.)$$

In Example 10(a) the coefficient of x^2 was a common factor of the sub-expression consisting of the terms in x^2 and x, but of course this is not always the case. For example, consider the quadratic expression

$$2x^2 + 5x + 1.$$

To complete the square in a quadratic like this, you begin by taking out the coefficient of x^2 from the sub-expression just as if it *were* a common factor – this will create fractions. For the quadratic here, you obtain

$$2\left(x^2 + \tfrac{5}{2}x\right) + 1.$$

You can then go on to complete the square using the method demonstrated in Example 10. The final answer is

$$2\left(x + \tfrac{5}{4}\right)^2 - \tfrac{17}{8}.$$

Activity 23   *Completing the square in quadratics of the form*
$ax^2 + bx + c$

Write the quadratic expressions below in completed-square form, and check your answers by multiplying out.

Use the completed-square forms to write down the vertices of the corresponding parabolas.

(a) $2x^2 - 4x - 1$ (b) $-x^2 - 8x - 18$

Here is a summary of the method that you have seen in this subsection.

Strategy   *To complete the square in a quadratic of the form*
$ax^2 + bx + c$

1. Rewrite the expression with the coefficient a of x^2 taken out of the $ax^2 + bx$ part as a factor. This generates a pair of brackets.

2. Complete the square in the simple quadratic inside the brackets, remembering to keep it enclosed within its brackets. This generates a second pair of brackets, inside the first pair.

3. Multiply out the *outer* brackets.

4. Collect the constant terms.

Writing the equation of a parabola in completed-square form gives you another way to find some of the information that you need to sketch it. You can read off the coordinates of the vertex immediately, and you can use the completed-square form to solve the quadratic equation that gives the x-intercepts.

In this section you have seen how to complete the square in any quadratic expression. You have seen that this method explains why the graphs of all quadratic functions are shifts of the graphs of equations of the form $y = ax^2$, and that it also explains why the quadratic formula works. You have also seen how to use the method to solve quadratic equations and to find vertices of parabolas.

5 Maximisation problems

In some real-life situations it is useful to find the maximum possible value of some quantity and to find the circumstances under which that maximum value is obtained. For example, a shopkeeper may want to know what his prices should be if he is to make the maximum possible profit. The problem of finding the maximum value of a quantity and the circumstances under which it is obtained is known as a **maximisation problem**.

If the situation can be modelled with a quadratic function, then the problem is solved by finding the vertex of its graph. You will see some examples of this in this section.

You have seen several methods for finding the vertex of the graph of a quadratic function in this unit. They are summarised in the box below.

To find the vertex of a parabola from its equation

To find the vertex of the parabola with equation $y = ax^2 + bx + c$, use any of the following methods.

- Use the formula $x = -b/(2a)$ to find the x-coordinate, then substitute into the equation of the parabola to find the y-coordinate.

- Find the x-intercepts (if there are any); then the value halfway between them is the x-coordinate of the vertex. Find the y-coordinate by substituting into the equation of the parabola.

- Complete the square: the parabola with equation $y = a(x - h)^2 + k$ has vertex (h, k).

- Plot the parabola using Graphplotter and read off the approximate coordinates of the vertex.

The fourth method of finding the vertex, plotting the parabola using Graphplotter, is useful if you need only approximate answers. It can also be a helpful way to check an answer that you have found using one of the other methods.

Often the trickiest part of solving a maximisation problem is finding a quadratic function that models the situation, and you will see some ideas for doing that in this section too.

5.1   The maximum height of a vertically-launched projectile

You have already seen how to model the motion of a vertically-launched projectile with a quadratic function. You saw in Subsection 3.4 that if a projectile is launched vertically upwards from an initial height h_0 with an initial speed v_0, then its height h after time t is given by the equation

$$h = -\tfrac{1}{2}gt^2 + v_0 t + h_0, \tag{12}$$

where g is the acceleration due to gravity (about $9.8 \, \text{m/s}^2$).

In the example below this model is used to find the maximum height reached by a distress flare fired vertically.

Example 11   *Finding the height reached by a distress flare*

A distress flare is fired vertically upwards from a height of $2\,\mathrm{m}$ at an initial speed of $52\,\mathrm{m/s}$. Find the height that it reaches, and the time that it takes to reach this height, to two significant figures.

Solution

The motion of the flare is modelled by equation (12) with $h_0 = 2$, $v_0 = 52$ and $g = 9.8$. So its height h in metres after t seconds is given by

$$h = -4.9t^2 + 52t + 2.$$

The maximum value of h is at the vertex of this parabola. The t-coordinate of the vertex is given by

$$t = -\frac{b}{2a},$$

where $a = -4.9$ and $b = 52$, so it is

$$t = -\frac{52}{2 \times (-4.9)} = 5.3061\ldots = 5.3 \text{ (to 2 s.f.)}.$$

Substituting $t = 5.3061\ldots$ into the equation of the parabola gives

$$\begin{aligned}
h &= -4.9t^2 + 52t + 2 \\
&= -4.9 \times (5.3061\ldots)^2 + 52 \times (5.3061\ldots) + 2 \\
&= 140 \text{ (to 2 s.f.)}.
\end{aligned}$$

So the vertex is approximately $(5.3, 140)$.

State a conclusion in the context of the question.

Hence the flare reaches a height of about 140 metres, and it takes about 5.3 seconds to reach this height.

As mentioned earlier, when you solve a problem like the one in Example 11, it is useful to check your answers using Graphplotter. Figure 35 shows a Graphplotter graph of the quadratic function in Example 11, and you can see that the vertex seems to be about $(5.3, 140)$, as expected.

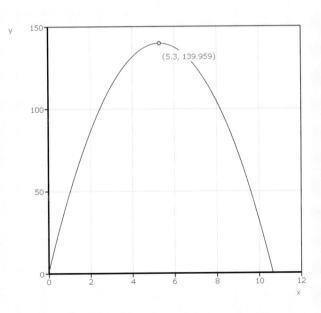

Figure 35   The graph of $y = -4.9x^2 + 52x + 2$

Here is a similar example for you to try.

Activity 24   *Finding the height reached by a ball thrown upwards*

A ball is thrown vertically upwards from a height of 1.6 m with an initial speed of 15 m/s. Find the maximum height reached by the ball, to the nearest metre.

Figure 36 Revenue against possible price increase

5.2 Maximising yields

Finding the maximum value of a quadratic function can help with decisions about how to maximise the yield from a business.

For example, the supplier of a saleable item or service can often increase the money that he makes – his *revenue* – by increasing his price. This may cause a drop in demand, but if the price increase is not too much, then the extra revenue from the increased price may outweigh the loss in revenue from the drop in demand. If the price increase is too much, however, then a large drop in demand can cause the overall revenue to decrease.

So as the possible price increase gets larger, the resulting revenue tends to increase and then decrease again, as illustrated in Figure 36. The optimum price increase can often be found by modelling the situation with a quadratic function, and finding the vertex. Here is an example to illustrate these ideas.

Example 12   *Maximising a boatman's revenue*

A boatman has 30 boats for hire. He finds that if he charges £20 an hour, then all his boats are hired, but generally for each £1 increase in the hire charge, one boat fewer is hired. Determine the amount by which the boatman should increase his price if he wants to maximise his revenue.

Solution

💭 Find a quadratic function to model the situation. The first step is to decide what the variables should be. 💭

The quantity that is to be maximised is the revenue, so denote that by £r.

The second variable could denote the price, rather than the price increase, but it is slightly easier to work with the increase.

The quantity that makes the revenue increase and decrease is the price increase, so denote that by £i.

💭 Now find a formula for r in terms of i. You might be able to write it down straight away. If not, try looking at a few numerical examples, like those in the table below. 💭

Price increase (£)	Hire price (£)	Number of boats hired	Revenue (£)
0	20	30	20×30
1	21	29	21×29
2	22	28	22×28
⋮	⋮	⋮	⋮

In general, if the price increase in £ is i, then the hire price in £ is $20 + i$, and the number of boats hired is $30 - i$. So the overall revenue per hour in £ is given by

$$r = (20 + i)(30 - i).$$

This is the equation of a parabola, with the right-hand side in factorised form. To find the value of i that gives the maximum value of r, you need to find the vertex of the parabola. Since the quadratic expression is already factorised, the quickest way to do this is to find the i-intercepts first.

Putting $r = 0$ gives

$$(20 + i)(30 - i) = 0.$$

Hence

$$i = -20 \quad \text{or} \quad i = 30,$$

so the i-intercepts are -20 and 30.

The value halfway between the i-intercepts is

$$\frac{-20 + 30}{2} = \frac{10}{2} = 5.$$

Substituting $i = 5$ into the equation of the parabola gives

$$r = (20 + i)(30 - i) = 25 \times 25 = 625.$$

So the vertex of the parabola is $(5, 625)$.

State a conclusion in the context of the problem.

The boatman can maximise his revenue by increasing his price by £5, to £25. Then his revenue is likely to be £625.

(Check: the vertex of the Graphplotter graph below is about $(5, 625)$.)

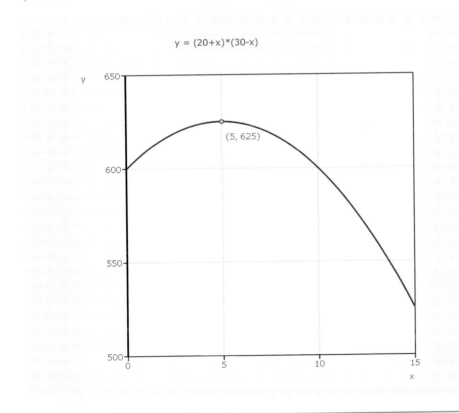

$y = (20+x)*(30-x)$

The Graphplotter graph that was used to check the answer to the example above was obtained by using 'Custom function', which is available from the drop-down list of equations. There is information about using Custom function in Section 2 of the MU123 Guide, and also on the Graphplotter Help page (press the orange 'Help' button at the top right of Graphplotter).

In Example 12 a quadratic model was used to help to maximise a financial yield. Models like this can also be used to help to maximise other types of yields, such as agricultural yields.

For example, consider a farmer who would like to maximise the yield from a fruit orchard. She may be able to increase the yield by increasing the number of trees, but if she increases the number of trees too much, then overcrowding will cause a large drop in the yield per tree, and the overall yield will fall.

Similarly, a dairy farmer may be able to increase the milk yield of his farm by increasing the number of cows in his fields, but if he increases the number of cows too much, then overcrowding will tend to decrease the milk yield per cow, causing the overall yield to fall. This is the scenario in the activity below.

Activity 25   Maximising milk yield

A dairy farmer wants to work out the number of cows that he should stock per hectare of grazing land to maximise the milk yield. The graph below, which he has seen in an agricultural magazine, gives the daily milk yield per cow that can be expected for different numbers of cows per hectare.

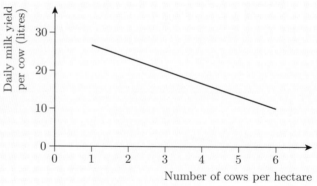

If the number of cows per hectare is denoted by n, and the daily milk yield per cow in litres is denoted by m, then the equation of the line on the graph is

$$m = -\tfrac{10}{3}n + 30.$$

(This equation can be found by using the methods that you learned in Unit 6.)

(a) Let y be the daily milk yield per hectare of grazing land, in litres. Find a formula for y in terms of n. You need to think about the number of cows on each hectare of land, and the daily milk yield from each of these cows.

(b) Hence determine the maximum daily milk yield per hectare, and the number of cows per hectare that will produce this yield.

(c) How many cows should the farmer stock on an 8-hectare field?

5.3 Maximising areas

In this subsection you will see two problems that involve maximising areas. You will see that it takes quite a lot of creative thought to solve the first problem, and it involves a number of different ideas that you have learned in the module. The second problem uses similar ideas, but it is a bit more straightforward, and you are asked to try to solve it yourself.

Example 13   *Maximising an area*

Tutorial clip

A farmer wants to construct an L-shaped enclosure with a boundary made up of fencing and two sides of a barn, as shown below. The barn is 8 m by 12 m, and the farmer has 100 m of fencing. What is the maximum area of the enclosure, and what are the dimensions of the enclosure with this maximum area?

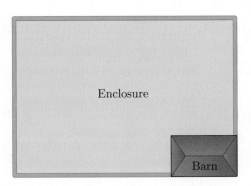

Solution

First choose the variables.

The quantity to be maximised is the area of the enclosure, so denote that by A m².

The quantity that makes the area increase and decrease is the length of the enclosure, so denote that by x m.

Now you need to find a formula for A in terms of x. To work out the area in terms of x you need to know the width of the enclosure, as well as its length, in terms of x. This is not obvious, so denote the width by y and use an equation to work it out. It helps to begin by drawing and labelling a diagram.

You might think that it is not just the length of the enclosure that makes the area increase and decrease, but also its width. However, because there is only 100 m of fencing, the greater the length, the smaller the width. So the area is determined by only one variable. This one variable could be either the length or the width.

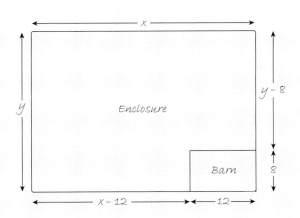

177

Since the total length of the fence is $100\,\text{m}$, we have

$$(x-12)+y+x+(y-8)=100.$$

💭 Simplify this equation and make y the subject. 💭

$$2x+2y-20=100$$
$$2y=120-2x$$
$$y=60-x$$

So the width of the field is $(60-x)\,\text{m}$.

💭 Now you can find a formula for A in terms of x. 💭

The total area of the field can be found by subtracting the area of the barn from the area of the larger rectangle. This gives

$$A=x(60-x)-8\times12,$$

which can be simplified to

$$A=60x-x^2-96$$
$$=-x^2+60x-96.$$

💭 The next step is to find the vertex of the parabola that is the graph of this equation. Let's do that by completing the square. 💭

Completing the square gives

$$A=-x^2+60x-96$$
$$=-(x^2-60x)-96$$
$$=-((x-30)^2-30^2)-96$$
$$=-((x-30)^2-900)-96$$
$$=-(x-30)^2+900-96$$
$$=-(x-30)^2+804.$$

So the vertex is $(30,804)$.

💭 State a conclusion in the context of the question. 💭

Hence the maximum area of the enclosure is $804\,\text{m}^2$, and this occurs when the length of the enclosure is $30\,\text{m}$ and the width is $(60-30)\,\text{m}=30\,\text{m}$.

Here is the activity for you to try.

Activity 26   *Maximising an area*

A farmer wants to make a rectangular enclosure next to an existing wall, using $120\,\text{m}$ of fencing. Let the area of the enclosure be $A\,\text{m}^2$, and let its width, as shown in the diagram below, be $x\,\text{m}$.

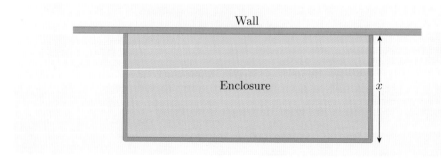

(a) Find an expression for the length of the enclosure in terms of x.

(b) Find a formula for A in terms of x.

(c) Hence find the maximum area of the enclosure, and the length and width that give this maximum area.

In this section you have seen some ideas for solving maximisation problems. Similar ideas can be used to solve **minimisation problems**, which are relevant for real-life situations that are modelled by u-shaped parabolas rather than n-shaped ones.

To end this section, here is a summary of the main steps used to solve a maximisation problem.

Strategy *To solve a maximisation problem*

1. Identify the quantity to be maximised and the quantity that it depends on, and denote each quantity by a variable.

2. Find a formula for the variable to be maximised in terms of the variable that it depends on.

3. If this gives a quadratic function, then find the vertex of its graph.

In this unit you have seen some quadratic models and their uses. You have learned about the graphs of quadratic functions, and how to sketch them, and you have also learned some new techniques for solving quadratic equations.

Learning checklist

After studying this unit, you should be able to:

- understand how some real-life situations can be modelled by quadratic functions

- understand the shapes and positions of the graphs of quadratic functions

- find the intercepts, axis of symmetry and vertex of the graph of a quadratic function from its equation

- sketch the graph of a quadratic function

- complete the square in quadratic expressions

- solve a quadratic equation by using the quadratic formula, by completing the square or by using an accurate graph

- determine the number of solutions of a quadratic equation from its coefficients

- construct simple quadratic models to describe real-life situations

- solve maximisation problems involving quadratic functions

- understand and apply Galileo's models for the motion of objects in free fall and projectiles launched horizontally or vertically.

Solutions and comments on Activities

Activity 1

Substituting $d = 26$ into the free-fall equation $d = 4.9t^2$ gives

$$26 = 4.9t^2.$$

Solving this equation gives

$$4.9t^2 = 26$$

$$t^2 = \frac{26}{4.9}$$

$$t = \sqrt{\frac{26}{4.9}} = 2.3 \text{ (to 1 d.p.)}.$$

(The positive square root is taken because the negative root does not make sense in this context.)

So the ball reaches the ground after about 2.3 seconds.

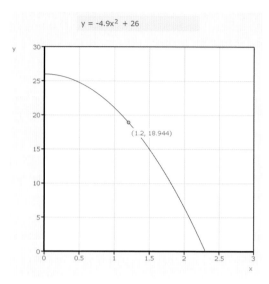

$y = -4.9x^2 + 26$

(1.2, 18.944)

Activity 2

(a) From Activity 1, you know that the ball takes less than 3 seconds to fall to the ground, so a reasonable range for the x-axis is 0 to 3.

The ball falls from a height of $26\,\text{m}$, so a reasonable range for the y-axis is 0 to 30.

The Graphplotter graph is shown below.

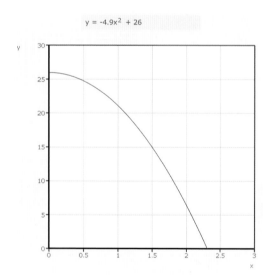

$y = -4.9x^2 + 26$

(b) The height of the ball above the ground after 1.2 seconds is approximately $19\,\text{m}$, as shown in the following Graphplotter graph.

Activity 3

(a) The time t seconds for the marble to hit the floor is given by the free-fall equation

$$d = 4.9t^2,$$

where $d = 0.8$, measured in metres.

Substituting into the equation and solving it gives

$$0.8 = 4.9t^2$$

$$4.9t^2 = 0.8$$

$$t^2 = \frac{0.8}{4.9}$$

$$t = \sqrt{\frac{0.8}{4.9}} = 0.4040\ldots = 0.40 \text{ (to 2 s.f.)}.$$

(The positive square root is taken because the negative one does not make sense in this context.)

So the marble will hit the floor after about $0.40\,\text{s}$.

(b) The horizontal distance that the marble will travel before hitting the floor is given by the equation

$$d = st,$$

where $s = 0.5$ and, from part (a), $t = 0.4040\ldots$, where the units are metres per second and seconds, respectively.

Substituting into the equation gives

$$d = 0.5 \times 0.4040\ldots = 0.20 \text{ (to 2 s.f.)}.$$

So the marble will travel about $0.20\,\text{m}$ before hitting the floor.

Activity 4

For example, one of the speeds given in Table 2 is 40 mph. Substituting $s = 40$ into formula (5), which is $B = \frac{1}{20}s^2$, gives

$$B = \frac{1}{20} \times 40^2 = 80.$$

So, according to the formula, a speed of 40 mph corresponds to a braking distance of 80 feet, which accords with the numbers given in Table 2.

Activity 5

(a) A table of values for the equation $y = -x^2$ is given below.

x	-3	-2	-1	0	1	2	3
y	-9	-4	-1	0	-1	-4	-9

(For example, substituting $x = -3$ into the equation gives $y = -(-3)^2 = -9$.)

The resulting graph is shown below.

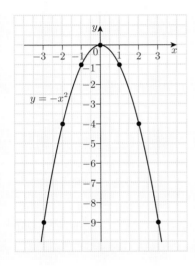

(b) The graph of $y = -x^2$ is a mirror image of the graph of $y = x^2$, reflected in the x-axis.

Activity 6

(a) Increasing the value of a within the positive values seems to make the parabola more narrow, while decreasing the value of a within the positive values seems to make it wider. The axis of symmetry is always the y-axis.

(b) Pairs of values of a that are negatives of each other give graphs that are reflections of each other in the x-axis, as expected.

So, as expected, increasing the *size* of a within the negative values seems to make the parabola narrower, while decreasing the size of a within the negative values seems to make it wider.

Activity 7

There are comments in the text after this activity.

Activity 8

(b) Changing c from 0 to 1 moves the graph up by 1 unit. The new graph crosses the y-axis at $(0, 1)$.

(c) The graph of $y = x^2 + c$ seems to be exactly the same as the graph of $y = x^2$, but shifted up or down the y-axis. It crosses the y-axis at $(0, c)$ (whether c is positive or negative).

(d) In general, whatever the values of a, b and c, the graph of $y = ax^2 + bx + c$ seems to be exactly the same as the graph of $y = ax^2 + bx$, but shifted vertically up or down, so that it crosses the y-axis at $(0, c)$.

Activity 9

The equation is $y = x^2 + 5x - 6$.

The coefficient of x^2 is positive, so the graph is u-shaped.

Putting $x = 0$ gives $y = -6$, so the y-intercept is -6.

Putting $y = 0$ gives

$$x^2 + 5x - 6 = 0$$
$$(x - 1)(x + 6) = 0$$
$$x - 1 = 0 \quad \text{or} \quad x + 6 = 0$$
$$x = 1 \quad \text{or} \quad x = -6.$$

So the x-intercepts are 1 and -6.

The value halfway between the x-intercepts is

$$\frac{1 + (-6)}{2} = \frac{-5}{2} = -2.5.$$

So the axis of symmetry is $x = -2.5$.

Substituting $x = -2.5$ into the equation of the parabola gives

$$y = x^2 + 5x - 6$$
$$= (-2.5)^2 + 5 \times (-2.5) - 6$$
$$= -12.25.$$

So the vertex is $(-2.5, -12.25)$.

A sketch of the graph is shown below.

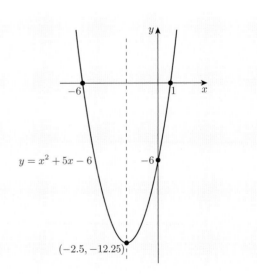

Activity 10

The equation is $y = 9x^2 - 6x + 1$.

The coefficient of x^2 is positive, so the graph is u-shaped.

Putting $x = 0$ gives $y = 1$, so the y-intercept is 1.

Putting $y = 0$ gives

$$9x^2 - 6x + 1 = 0$$
$$(3x - 1)(3x - 1) = 0$$
$$3x - 1 = 0$$
$$x = \tfrac{1}{3}.$$

So the only x-intercept is $\tfrac{1}{3}$.

Therefore the axis of symmetry is $x = \tfrac{1}{3}$, and the vertex is $\left(\tfrac{1}{3}, 0\right)$.

A sketch of the graph is shown below.

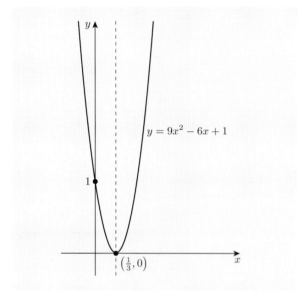

(If you feel uncomfortable basing your sketch on just two points, then you can calculate a third point on the parabola. For example, substituting $x = 1$ into the equation gives

$$y = 9 \times 1^2 - 6 \times 1 + 1 = 4,$$

so you can plot the point $(1, 4)$ to make the shape of the parabola clearer.)

Activity 11

The equation is $y = x^2 + 2x + 3$.

The coefficient of x^2 is positive, so the graph is u-shaped.

Putting $x = 0$ gives $y = 3$, so the y-intercept is 3.

The equation of the axis of symmetry is $x = -b/(2a)$, where $a = 1$ and $b = 2$, so it is

$$x = -\frac{2}{2 \times 1}; \quad \text{that is,} \quad x = -1.$$

Substituting $x = -1$ into the equation of the parabola gives

$$y = x^2 + 2x + 3$$
$$= (-1)^2 + 2 \times (-1) + 3$$
$$= 1 - 2 + 3$$
$$= 2.$$

So the vertex is $(-1, 2)$.

A sketch of the graph is shown below.

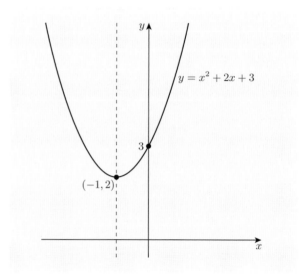

Activity 12

(a) The graph of $y = -x^2 + 2x + 7$ is shown below.

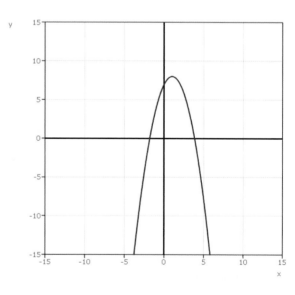

(b) The solutions of the equation $-x^2 + 2x + 7 = 0$ are $x = -1.83$ and $x = 3.83$ (to 2 d.p.).

Activity 13

You should have found that the point with x-coordinate 1.10 has a y-coordinate greater than 20, while the point with x-coordinate 1.11 has a y-coordinate less than 20. (The x-coordinate 1.10 is displayed as 1.1 even if you have zoomed in enough for x-coordinates to be displayed to two decimal places, because Graphplotter does not display trailing zeros.)

Hence the point whose y-coordinate is exactly 20 has x-coordinate 1.1, to one decimal place.

So the ball takes approximately 1.1 seconds to fall to a height of 20 m.

Activity 14

(a) The equation is
$$x^2 + 6x + 1 = 0,$$
so $a = 1$, $b = 6$ and $c = 1$.

The quadratic formula gives
$$\begin{aligned}
x &= \frac{-b \pm \sqrt{b^2 - 4ac}}{2a} \\
&= \frac{-6 \pm \sqrt{6^2 - 4 \times 1 \times 1}}{2 \times 1} \\
&= \frac{-6 \pm \sqrt{36 - 4}}{2} \\
&= \frac{-6 \pm \sqrt{32}}{2} \\
&= \frac{-6 \pm 4\sqrt{2}}{2} \\
&= -3 \pm 2\sqrt{2}.
\end{aligned}$$

So the solutions are $x = -3 + 2\sqrt{2}$ and $x = -3 - 2\sqrt{2}$.

(b) The equation is
$$3x^2 - 8x - 2 = 0,$$
so $a = 3$, $b = -8$ and $c = -2$.

The quadratic formula gives
$$\begin{aligned}
x &= \frac{-b \pm \sqrt{b^2 - 4ac}}{2a} \\
&= \frac{-(-8) \pm \sqrt{(-8)^2 - 4 \times 3 \times (-2)}}{2 \times 3} \\
&= \frac{8 \pm \sqrt{64 + 24}}{6} \\
&= \frac{8 \pm \sqrt{88}}{6} \\
&= \frac{8 \pm 2\sqrt{22}}{6} \\
&= \frac{4 \pm \sqrt{22}}{3}.
\end{aligned}$$

So the solutions are $x = \dfrac{4 + \sqrt{22}}{3}$ and $x = \dfrac{4 - \sqrt{22}}{3}$.

Activity 15

The equation is
$$-x^2 = -x - \tfrac{3}{2}.$$
Clearing the fraction gives
$$-2x^2 = -2x - 3.$$
This equation can be rearranged as follows.
$$\begin{aligned}
0 &= 2x^2 - 2x - 3 \\
2x^2 - 2x - 3 &= 0
\end{aligned}$$
So $a = 2$, $b = -2$ and $c = -3$.

The quadratic formula gives
$$\begin{aligned}
x &= \frac{-b \pm \sqrt{b^2 - 4ac}}{2a} \\
&= \frac{-(-2) \pm \sqrt{(-2)^2 - 4 \times 2 \times (-3)}}{2 \times 2} \\
&= \frac{2 \pm \sqrt{4 + 24}}{4} \\
&= \frac{2 \pm \sqrt{28}}{4} \\
&= \frac{2 \pm 2\sqrt{7}}{4} \\
&= \frac{1 \pm \sqrt{7}}{2}.
\end{aligned}$$

So the solutions are $x = \dfrac{1 + \sqrt{7}}{2}$ and $x = \dfrac{1 - \sqrt{7}}{2}$.

Activity 16

(a) The width of the photograph is 12 inches, and there are x inches of white border on each side, so the width of the backboard is $12 + 2x$ inches. Similarly, the height of the photograph is 18 inches, and there are x inches of white border both above and below, so the height of the backboard is $18 + 2x$ inches.

(b) The area of the photograph is
$$\text{width} \times \text{height} = 12 \times 18 = 216 \text{ in}^2.$$
The area of the backboard is 150% of the area of the photograph, so its area is
$$150\% \text{ of } 216 = 1.5 \times 216 = 324 \text{ in}^2.$$

(c) The area of the backboard in terms of x is
$$\begin{aligned}
\text{width} \times \text{height} &= (12 + 2x)(18 + 2x) \\
&= 216 + 24x + 36x + 4x^2 \\
&= 4x^2 + 60x + 216,
\end{aligned}$$
where the units are square inches.

(d) Using the answers to parts (b) and (c) gives

$$4x^2 + 60x + 216 = 324.$$

This equation can be rearranged as follows.

$$4x^2 + 60x - 108 = 0$$
$$x^2 + 15x - 27 = 0$$

(e) The equation in part (d) cannot easily be factorised, so we use the quadratic formula.

We have $a = 1$, $b = 15$ and $c = -27$.

Using the quadratic formula gives

$$
\begin{aligned}
x &= \frac{-b \pm \sqrt{b^2 - 4ac}}{2a} \\
&= \frac{-15 \pm \sqrt{15^2 - 4 \times 1 \times (-27)}}{2 \times 1} \\
&= \frac{-15 \pm \sqrt{225 + 108}}{2} \\
&= \frac{-15 \pm \sqrt{333}}{2} \\
&= \frac{-15 \pm 3\sqrt{37}}{2} \\
&= \frac{-15 + 3\sqrt{37}}{2} \quad \text{or} \quad \frac{-15 - 3\sqrt{37}}{2} \\
&= 1.624\ldots \quad \text{or} \quad -16.624\ldots.
\end{aligned}
$$

Only the positive solution makes sense in the context of the problem. So the width of the white border is 1.6 inches, to the nearest tenth of an inch.

The width of the backboard is

$$12 + 2 \times 1.624\ldots = 15.2\,\text{in},$$

and its height is

$$18 + 2 \times 1.624\ldots = 21.2\,\text{in},$$

to the nearest tenth of an inch.

Activity 17

(a) The equation is

$$9x^2 + 30x + 25 = 0,$$

so $a = 9$, $b = 30$ and $c = 25$.

The discriminant is

$$
\begin{aligned}
b^2 - 4ac &= 30^2 - 4 \times 9 \times 25 \\
&= 900 - 900 \\
&= 0.
\end{aligned}
$$

Since the discriminant is 0, there is one solution.

The equation can be solved by factorising, as below. Since there is only one solution, the two linear expressions in the factorisation must be the same (or one must be a multiple of the other – that is, it must be the other multiplied through by some number).

$$9x^2 + 30x + 25 = 0$$
$$(3x + 5)(3x + 5) = 0$$
$$(3x + 5)^2 = 0$$
$$3x + 5 = 0$$
$$x = -\tfrac{5}{3}$$

(b) The equation is

$$x^2 - 4x - 2 = 0,$$

so $a = 1$, $b = -4$ and $c = -2$.

The discriminant is

$$
\begin{aligned}
b^2 - 4ac &= (-4)^2 - 4 \times 1 \times (-2) \\
&= 16 - (-8) \\
&= 24.
\end{aligned}
$$

Since the discriminant is greater than zero, there are two solutions.

The equation cannot be easily factorised, so we solve it by using the quadratic formula. This gives

$$
\begin{aligned}
x &= \frac{-b \pm \sqrt{b^2 - 4ac}}{2a} \\
&= \frac{-(-4) \pm \sqrt{24}}{2 \times 1} \\
&= \frac{4 \pm 2\sqrt{6}}{2} \\
&= 2 \pm \sqrt{6}.
\end{aligned}
$$

The solutions are $x = 2 + \sqrt{6}$ and $x = 2 - \sqrt{6}$.

(The value of $b^2 - 4ac$ was already worked out before the quadratic formula was used, so this value was just substituted in, instead of working it out again.)

(c) The equation can be rearranged as follows.

$$-3x^2 + 5x = 4$$
$$3x^2 - 5x + 4 = 0$$

So $a = 3$, $b = -5$ and $c = 4$.

The discriminant is

$$b^2 - 4ac = (-5)^2 - 4 \times 3 \times 4 = 25 - 48 = -23.$$

Since the discriminant is less than zero, there are no solutions.

Activity 18

The height h metres of the rocket after time t seconds is given by the formula

$$h = -\tfrac{1}{2}gt^2 + v_0 t + h_0,$$

with $h_0 = 155$, $v_0 = 49$ and $g = 9.8$. So

$$h = -4.9t^2 + 49t + 155.$$

The rocket returns to the ground when $h = 0$, so we must solve the equation

$$-4.9t^2 + 49t + 155 = 0.$$

Multiplying through by -1 gives
$$4.9t^2 - 49t - 155 = 0.$$

We use the quadratic formula, with $a = 4.9$, $b = -49$ and $c = -155$. This gives
$$\begin{aligned}
t &= \frac{-b \pm \sqrt{b^2 - 4ac}}{2a} \\
&= \frac{-(-49) \pm \sqrt{(-49)^2 - 4 \times 4.9 \times (-155)}}{2 \times 4.9} \\
&= \frac{49 \pm \sqrt{2401 + 3038}}{9.8} \\
&= \frac{49 \pm \sqrt{5439}}{9.8} \\
&= -2.5 \quad \text{or} \quad 12.5 \quad \text{(to 1 d.p.).}
\end{aligned}$$

The negative solution does not make sense in this context, so we disregard it. So the time taken for the rocket to reach the ground is about 12.5 seconds.

Activity 19

(a) The parabola is u-shaped.

Its vertex is $(-1, 5)$.

(b) The parabola is n-shaped.

Its vertex is $(-3, 7)$.

(c) The parabola is u-shaped.

Its vertex is $(1, -4)$.

(d) The parabola is n-shaped.

Its vertex is $\left(-\frac{1}{2}, -1\right)$.

(e) The parabola is u-shaped.

Its vertex is $(0, 3)$.

(f) The parabola is u-shaped.

Its vertex is $(2, 0)$.

Activity 20

(a) $\begin{aligned}[t]
x^2 + 16x &= (x + 8)^2 - 8^2 \\
&= (x + 8)^2 - 64
\end{aligned}$

(Check: $\begin{aligned}[t]
(x + 8)^2 - 64 &= (x + 8)(x + 8) - 64 \\
&= x^2 + 16x + 64 - 64 \\
&= x^2 + 16x.)
\end{aligned}$

(b) $\begin{aligned}[t]
x^2 - 12x &= (x - 6)^2 - (-6)^2 \\
&= (x - 6)^2 - 36
\end{aligned}$

(Check: $\begin{aligned}[t]
(x - 6)^2 - 36 &= (x - 6)(x - 6) - 36 \\
&= x^2 - 12x + 36 - 36 \\
&= x^2 - 12x.)
\end{aligned}$

(c) $\begin{aligned}[t]
t^2 - 2t &= (t - 1)^2 - (-1)^2 \\
&= (t - 1)^2 - 1
\end{aligned}$

(Check: $\begin{aligned}[t]
(t - 1)^2 - 1 &= (t - 1)(t - 1) - 1 \\
&= t^2 - 2t + 1 - 1 \\
&= t^2 - 2t.)
\end{aligned}$

(d) $\begin{aligned}[t]
x^2 + 3x &= \left(x + \tfrac{3}{2}\right)^2 - \left(\tfrac{3}{2}\right)^2 \\
&= \left(x + \tfrac{3}{2}\right)^2 - \tfrac{9}{4}
\end{aligned}$

(Check: $\begin{aligned}[t]
\left(x + \tfrac{3}{2}\right)^2 - \tfrac{9}{4} &= \left(x + \tfrac{3}{2}\right)\left(x + \tfrac{3}{2}\right) - \tfrac{9}{4} \\
&= x^2 + \tfrac{3}{2}x + \tfrac{3}{2}x + \tfrac{9}{4} - \tfrac{9}{4} \\
&= x^2 + 3x.)
\end{aligned}$

Activity 21

(a) $\begin{aligned}[t]
x^2 + 6x - 3 &= (x + 3)^2 - 9 - 3 \\
&= (x + 3)^2 - 12
\end{aligned}$

(Check: $\begin{aligned}[t]
(x + 3)^2 - 12 &= x^2 + 6x + 9 - 12 \\
&= x^2 + 6x - 3.)
\end{aligned}$

(b) $\begin{aligned}[t]
x^2 - 4x + 9 &= (x - 2)^2 - 4 + 9 \\
&= (x - 2)^2 + 5
\end{aligned}$

(Check: $\begin{aligned}[t]
(x - 2)^2 + 5 &= x^2 - 4x + 4 + 5 \\
&= x^2 - 4x + 9.)
\end{aligned}$

(c) $\begin{aligned}[t]
p^2 - 12p - 5 &= (p - 6)^2 - 36 - 5 \\
&= (p - 6)^2 - 41
\end{aligned}$

(Check: $\begin{aligned}[t]
(p - 6)^2 - 41 &= p^2 - 12p + 36 - 41 \\
&= p^2 - 12p - 5.)
\end{aligned}$

(d) $\begin{aligned}[t]
x^2 + x + 1 &= \left(x + \tfrac{1}{2}\right)^2 - \tfrac{1}{4} + 1 \\
&= \left(x + \tfrac{1}{2}\right)^2 + \tfrac{3}{4}
\end{aligned}$

(Check: $\begin{aligned}[t]
\left(x + \tfrac{1}{2}\right)^2 + \tfrac{3}{4} &= x^2 + x + \tfrac{1}{4} + \tfrac{3}{4} \\
&= x^2 + x + 1.)
\end{aligned}$

Activity 22

(a) $\begin{aligned}[t]
x^2 + 6x - 5 &= 0 \\
(x + 3)^2 - 9 - 5 &= 0 \\
(x + 3)^2 - 14 &= 0 \\
(x + 3)^2 &= 14 \\
x + 3 &= \pm\sqrt{14} \\
x &= -3 \pm \sqrt{14}
\end{aligned}$

The solutions are $x = -3 + \sqrt{14}$ and $x = -3 - \sqrt{14}$.

(b) $2x^2 - 12x - 5 = 0$

$x^2 - 6x - \frac{5}{2} = 0$

$(x-3)^2 - 9 - \frac{5}{2} = 0$

$(x-3)^2 - \frac{18}{2} - \frac{5}{2} = 0$

$(x-3)^2 - \frac{23}{2} = 0$

$(x-3)^2 = \frac{23}{2}$

$x - 3 = \pm\sqrt{\frac{23}{2}}$

$x = 3 \pm \sqrt{\frac{23}{2}}$

The solutions are $x = 3 + \sqrt{\frac{23}{2}}$ and $x = 3 - \sqrt{\frac{23}{2}}$.

Activity 23

(a) $2x^2 - 4x - 1 = 2(x^2 - 2x) - 1$

$= 2((x-1)^2 - 1) - 1$

$= 2(x-1)^2 - 2 - 1$

$= 2(x-1)^2 - 3$

(Check: $2(x-1)^2 - 3 = 2(x^2 - 2x + 1) - 3$

$= 2x^2 - 4x + 2 - 3$

$= 2x^2 - 4x - 1.$)

The vertex of the parabola with equation
$y = 2x^2 - 4x - 1$ is $(1, -3)$.

(b) $-x^2 - 8x - 18 = -(x^2 + 8x) - 18$

$= -((x+4)^2 - 16) - 18$

$= -(x+4)^2 + 16 - 18$

$= -(x+4)^2 - 2$

(Check: $-(x+4)^2 - 2 = -(x^2 + 8x + 16) - 2$

$= -x^2 - 8x - 16 - 2$

$= -x^2 - 8x - 18.$)

The vertex of the parabola with equation
$y = -x^2 - 8x - 18$ is $(-4, -2)$.

Activity 24

The motion of the ball is modelled by the equation

$h = -\frac{1}{2}gt^2 + v_0t + h_0$

with $h_0 = 1.6$, $v_0 = 15$ and $g = 9.8$. So its height
in metres after t seconds is given by

$h = -4.9t^2 + 15t + 1.6.$

The maximum value of h is at the vertex of this
parabola.

The t-coordinate of the vertex is given by

$t = -\frac{b}{2a},$

where $a = -4.9$ and $b = 15$, so it is

$t = -\frac{15}{2 \times (-4.9)} = 1.5306\ldots.$

Substituting $t = 1.5306\ldots$ into the equation of the
parabola gives

$h = -4.9t^2 + 15t + 1.6$

$= -4.9 \times (1.5306\ldots)^2 + 15 \times (1.5306\ldots) + 1.6$

$= 13.079\ldots$

$= 13$ (to the nearest whole number).

So the ball reaches a height of approximately $13\,\text{m}$.

(This answer can be checked using the
Graphplotter graph below.)

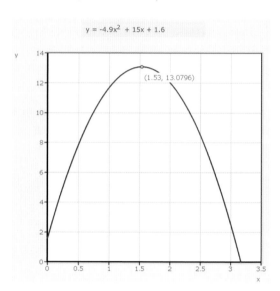

Activity 25

(a) There are n cows per hectare, and each cow
produces m litres of milk per day, where m is given
by the formula in the question. So y, the total
daily milk yield per hectare, in litres, is given by

$y = n \times m,$

that is,

$y = n\left(-\frac{10}{3}n + 30\right).$

(b) We have to find the vertex of the parabola
that is the graph of the equation found in part (a).
We do this by finding the n-intercepts first, since
the expression on the right-hand side of the
equation is already factorised.

Putting $y = 0$ gives

$n\left(-\frac{10}{3}n + 30\right) = 0,$

so

$n = 0 \quad \text{or} \quad -\frac{10}{3}n + 30 = 0.$

Solving the linear equation on the right gives

$-\frac{10}{3}n = -30$

$\frac{10}{3}n = 30$

$n = 30 \times \frac{3}{10}$

$n = 9.$

So the n-intercepts are 0 and 9.

The value halfway between the n-intercepts is 4.5.
Substituting $n = 4.5$ into the equation of the parabola gives

$$y = 4.5 \times \left(-\tfrac{10}{3} \times 4.5 + 30\right)$$
$$= 4.5 \times (-15 + 30)$$
$$= 67.5.$$

So the vertex of the parabola is $(4.5, 67.5)$.

Hence the farmer can maximise the milk yield by stocking 4.5 cows per hectare. (Though the number of cows in a field will need to be rounded to a whole number, of course!) At a stocking rate of 4.5 cows per hectare, the daily milk yield will be 67.5 litres per hectare.

(This answer can be checked using the Graphplotter graph below, which was produced by using 'Custom function'.)

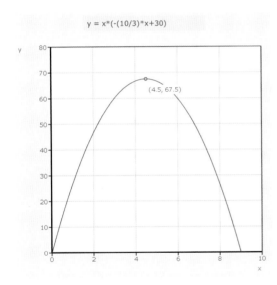

(c) The number of cows that the farmer should stock on an 8-hectare field is $8 \times 4.5 = 36$.

Activity 26

(a) The total length of fencing is $120\,\text{m}$, and two of the three sides of the enclosure are $x\,\text{m}$ long. So the length of the third side is $(120 - 2x)\,\text{m}$, and this is the length of the enclosure.

(b) The area of the enclosure is given by
$$A = x(120 - 2x).$$

(c) The formula found in part (b) is already factorised, so the quickest way to find the vertex is to find the x-intercepts first.

Putting $A = 0$ gives
$$x(120 - 2x) = 0,$$
so
$$x = 0 \quad \text{or} \quad x = \frac{120}{2} = 60.$$

So the x-intercepts are 0 and 60.

The value halfway between the x-intercepts is 30.

Substituting $x = 30$ into the equation of the parabola gives
$$A = 30(120 - 2 \times 30) = 30(120 - 60)$$
$$= 30 \times 60 = 1800.$$

So the vertex is $(30, 1800)$.

Hence the maximum area of the enclosure is $1800\,\text{m}^2$, and this is achieved when the width is $30\,\text{m}$ and the length is $(120 - 2 \times 30)\,\text{m} = 60\,\text{m}$.

(This answer can be checked using the GraphPlotter graph below, which was produced by using 'Custom function'.)

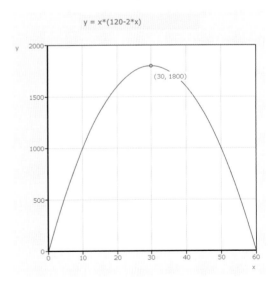

Acknowledgements

Grateful acknowledgement is made to the following sources for permission to reproduce material in this book.

Unit 8

Cartoon on page 8 © ScienceCartoonsPlus.com; Figure (b) in Activity 19 © Leo Reynolds on www.flickr.com; Figure (c) in Activity 19 © travel.webshots.com; Figure (d) in Activity 19 Saturn Parts Wholesale.com; Figure 23 © iStockphoto; Figure 24 © Neil Paterson; Figure 28 © angus@pobox.com; Figure 61 © 2008 – Advameg Inc; Figure 75 © www.wikipedia.org; Figure 76: Taken from www.wikipedia.org and used under Creative Commons.

Unit 9

Cartoon on page 72 © ScienceCartoonsPlus.com; Figure 3 © W & W Medsystems Ltd; Figure 8 © Arthur Benjamin; Alan Johnson quote on page 88 © Parliamentary copyright 2008; Figure 9 © Thomas Harriot Seminar 2008, Design: Peter J. Forshaw, Wikipedia; Cartoon on page 103 © 2001–2009 Mark Anderson; Cartoon on page 115 © 2001–2009 Mark Anderson.

Unit 10

Figure 1: Portrait of Galileo Galilei by Justus Sustermans, Royal Maritime Museum, Greenwich. © Flickr Photo Sharing; Figure 2: Reconstruction of Galileo's laboratory at the Deutsches Museum, Munich. © 1995–2008, American Physical Society; Figure 4: Portrait of Isaac Newton by Barrington Bramley, after Godfrey Kneller. Taken from www.wikimedia.org; Figure 6(a) © Brian Talbot/Flickr.com. This file is licensed under the Creative Commons Attribution ShareAlike 2.0 http://creativecommons.org/licenses/by-nc/2.0/;
Figure 6(b): Courtesy of D. Phillips, Faculty of Mathematics, Computing and Technology, Interfaculty Electronics and Computing, Open University; Figure 6(c) © Steve Bowbrick/Flickr.com. This file is licensed under the Creative Commons Attribution ShareAlike 2.0 http://creativecommons.org/licenses/by-nc-sa/2.0/; Figures 10(a) and (b) © Museum of the History of Science, Oxford; Figure 12: Stillman Drake *Galileo's notes on motion*, monograph 5, Annali dell'Istituto e Museo di Storia della Scienza (Florence, 1979), p. 79; Figures 14 and 15 © 2009 Associated Newspapers Ltd; Figure 17 © Museum of the History of Science, Oxford; Figure 18 © Chris Aspinwall; Figure 20: Crown copyright material reproduced under Class Licence Number C01W0000065 with the permission of the Controller of HMSO and the Queen's Printer for Scotland; Figure in Activity 16 on page 155 © Katarina Stefanovic/Flickr Photo Sharing; Figure 32: Michael Maggs, Richard Bartz (ed) from www.wikipedia.org. This file is licensed under the Creative Commons Attribution ShareAlike 3.0 http://creativecommons.org/licenses/by-sa/3.0/.

INDEX

acceleration due to gravity   129
acute angle   10
adding algebraic fractions   105
air resistance   130
algebraic fraction   103
algebraic fractions
    equations involving   110
alternate (Z) angles   14
angle
    acute, obtuse, etc.   10
    alternate (Z)   14
    corresponding (F)   14
    on a straight line   10
    opposite (X)   13
apex angle of an isosceles triangle   19
apex of a cone   59
Apollonius   130
arc of a circle   54
Archimedes' method for approximating π 56
area
    of a circle   56
    of a parallelogram   49
    of a rectangle   48
    of a shape   48
    of a trapezium   51
    of a triangle   50
argument, geometric   18
arithmetic progression   75
arithmetic sequence   75
    (common) difference   75
    sum   75
axiom   8
axis of symmetry of a parabola   138
    formula for   147

Babylonians   89
ballistics   132
base
    of a parallelogram   49
    of a triangle   49
base angles of an isosceles triangle   19
bisect   36
Bombelli, Rafael   158
box   59
brackets
    multiplying out   82
    squaring   84
braking distance   136

cancelling algebraic fractions   103, 104
capacity   60
centre of a circle   54
centre of rotation   27
chord of a circle   54
circle   54
    area   56
    circumference   54, 55
circumference of a circle   54, 55
circumscribed polygon   56

clearing algebraic fractions   110
coefficient of a quadratic expression   87
common denominator of algebraic fractions   105
common difference   75
completed-square form   162
completing the square   162
cone   59, 61
congruent shapes   28
congruent triangles   30
    conditions for   34
construction (geometric)   17
construction line   17
converse of a result   16
corresponding (F) angles   14
corresponding angles of congruent triangles   30
corresponding sides of triangles   34
corresponding vertices of congruent triangles   30
cube   59
cuboid   59, 61
cylinder   59, 61

decagon   23
degree (measure of an angle)   9
depth of a solid   58
diameter of a circle   54
difference (common)   75
difference of two squares   86
dimensionless quantity   54
discriminant   157
dividing algebraic fractions   107

equilateral triangle   19
    angles   19
equivalent fractions   103
Euclid   8
Euclid's *Elements*   8
expanding pairs of brackets   82

F angles   14
factor of a quadratic expression   91
factor pair   92
factorising a quadratic expression   91
finite sequence   75
formulas, rearranging   112, 115
fraction, algebraic   103
free fall   127
free-fall equation   129
function   138
    quadratic   138

Galileo   126
geometric argument   18
golden ratio   156
golden rectangle   156
graph of quadratic function   141, 143

height of a solid   58
hemisphere   62
heptagon   23
hexagon   23

horizontally-launched projectile   133, 135
hypotenuse   43

identity   80
inclined plane   127
included angle in a triangle   32
included side in a triangle   32
infinite sequence   75
inscribed polygon   56
intercepts of a parabola   143
interior angle
    of a polygon   25
    of a triangle   17
isosceles triangle   19

kite   24

line (in geometry)   9
line of symmetry   28
line segment   9
line symmetry   28

magnitude of a number   140
maximisation problem   172
    area   177–179
    projectile height   172–174
    solving   179
    yield   174–176
minimisation problem   179
mirror line   28
mirror symmetry   28
model, quadratic   130
multiplying fractions   107
multiplying out pairs of brackets   82

n-shaped parabola   141
net of a solid   60
Newton, Isaac   129
nonagon   23

oblong number   78
obtuse angle   10
octagon   23
odd numbers, sum of   72
opposite (X) angles   13
opposite angles of a quadrilateral   23
order of a rotational symmetry   27

parabola   129
    axis of symmetry   138, 147
    intercepts   143
    n-shaped   141
    shifting   160
    u-shaped   141
    vertex   138, 163, 172
parabolic curve   129
parallelogram   24
    area   49
pentagon   23
perfect square   95
perimeter of a shape   48
perpendicular   47

perpendicular height
    of a parallelogram   49
    of a triangle   49
perpendicular lines   49
plane   9
plane shape   48
point   9
polygon   23
    angle sum   25
    interior angle   25
    regular   25
polygonal shape   58
prism   58, 61
projectile   132
    horizontally-launched   133, 135
    maximum height of vertically-launched   173
    motion of vertically-launched   159
    range of horizontally-launched   134
    vertically-launched   158
Pythagoras' Theorem   43
    proof   46
Pythagorean triple   46
Pythagoreans   79

quadratic equation   88
    number of solutions   157
    simplifying   99
    solving by completing the square   167
    solving by factorising   96
    solving by formula   152
    solving graphically   148
quadratic expression   87
    factorising   91, 92, 97
quadratic formula   152
    derivation   168
quadratic function   138
    graph   141, 143
    sketching the graph   144–148
quadratic model   130
quadrilateral   23

radius of a circle   54
reciprocal of an algebraic fraction   107
rectangle   24
    area   48
reflection line   28
reflex angle   10
regular polygon   25
repeated solution of a quadratic equation   96
revenue   174
rhombus   24
right angle   9, 10
right-angled triangle   19
rotational symmetry   27

scale factor   29
scalene triangle   20
sector of a circle   54
segment of a circle   54
semicircle   55
sequence   75
shape

congruent   28
plane   48
similar   29
solid   58
similar shapes   29
similar triangles   38
size of a number   140
slant height of a cone   59
solid   58
sphere   61
square   24
squaring brackets   84
stopping distance   136
straight angle   10
subtracting algebraic fractions   105
surface area   60
formulas for   61
symmetry
axis of   138
line (mirror)   28
line of   28
rotational   27

term of a sequence   75
terminal velocity   130
thinking distance   136
three-dimensional shape   58
trailing zeros   152
trajectory of a projectile   132
trapezium   24

area   51
triangle   17
angle sum   17
area   50
congruent   30
equilateral   19
interior angle   17
isosceles   19
right-angled   19
scalene   20
similar   38
triangular number   74
triangular prism   58
two-dimensional shape   58

u-shaped parabola   141

vertex (in geometry)   9
vertex of a parabola   138
finding   162, 163, 172
vertically-launched projectile   158
volume   60
formulas for   61

width of a solid   58
wiggliness   53

X angles   13

Z angles   14